AN ILLUSTRA
INTRODUCTION TO THE

LARGER FUNGI
OF
NORTH CYPRUS

D.E. VINEY
2005

To:

Matthew, Peter, Anne-Marie,

Connie, Ruth and Faith

Published by Kevin Viney, 122 East Street, Olney, Bucks, MK46 4BT

Text © D.E. Viney 2005
Illustrations © D.E. Viney 2005
Photographs © D.E. Viney 2005

ISBN 0 85546 109 8

Distributed by The Richmond Publishing Co. Ltd.,
P.O. Box 963, Slough SL2 3RS England
Telephone 00 44 (0)1753 643104
Fax 00 44 (0)1753 646553
email rpc@richmond.co.uk

Printed in Great Britain

Contents

Foreword

In his foreword to the illustrated guide to North Cyprus sedges, grasses and ferns, my colleague Dr Tom Cope congratulated Deryck Viney on tackling a notoriously 'difficult' group of plants, previously covered only by the scholarly Flora of Cyprus, and making them accessible to a wider public.

With the present volume, Deryck has ventured even further afield, leaving the well-charted kingdom of the plants behind and bravely entering the mysterious realms of the fungal kingdom with no guide other than his own enthusiasm, dedication and perseverance.

The result is not only an attractively illustrated field book, but, by necessity, a volume of entirely original research: the first book ever to be written on the larger fungi of Cyprus and one of the first to cover any part of the eastern Mediterranean area, most of which is still mycological Terra Incognita.

Deryck has seen this more as a challenge than a problem, and quite right too. The 'difficulty' of fungi is largely to do with the unpredictable and short-lived appearance of their fruitbodies (mushrooms, toadstools, puffballs, and the rest) and partly with the sheer number and variety of species that may be encountered. But this 'difficulty' is also part of the pleasure. Looking for fungi is an activity full of surprises, and no matter how many seasons you spend in the field these surprises never stop. Your own back garden, the local woods and fields, even the dullest roadside verge can – after years of familiarity – suddenly produce a crop of strange and intriguing fruitbodies you have never seen before.

We can guarantee that the present volume will not cover all the surprises that lie in wait for fungus forayers in North Cyprus. But it is an excellent introduction to the variety and scope of the larger fungi that may be found here, from earthstars and stinkhorns to edible mushrooms and morels, all admirably illustrated with Deryck's own line drawings and colour photographs.

Encouraging naturalists and field workers to become enthusiasts for fungi is a worthy cause indeed. Let's hope Deryck's new guide finds the appreciative audience it fully deserves.

Dr Peter Roberts
Mycology Section
Royal Botanic Gardens
Kew

Preface

We can confidently assert that this is the first of its kind treating the fungi of Cyprus. Mycologists constitute a tight little society, each one knowing the others, so if an earlier attempt had been made we should surely have known about it.

Cyprus, moreover, covers an isolated and relatively small area, so that its fungi are 'personally' known to each other – a small but stable group.

We have deliberately tried to keep the book as brief as possible by interpreting the concept of 'species' fairly tightly, so we hereby launch it amongst its equally select but enthusiastic readership.

May they not be disappointed!

D.E.Viney

Acknowledgements

Although it is impossible to mention all those whose kindness and friendship have helped in the production of this book; the author would like to acknowledge the help of the friends and colleagues in North Cyprus; in particular the North Cyprus Forestry Department for their continued encouragement, Christina Hessenberg, Nadine Miller and Mustafa Merakli whose assistance in finding fungal specimens has been vital to this project; and Kazım Kazımoğlu for much help and advice (including Turkish nomenclature), during our long friendship.

Special thanks go to the many specialists who have identified specimens and who have advised: particular thanks go to Dr Peter Roberts, Dr Brian Spooner at the Royal Botanic Gardens Kew. Dr Derek Schafer (*Coprinus*) Dr Tom Hering (*Psathyrella*), Bert Brand (*Agaricus*), Alan Rayner, Alan Hills (*Boletus*) Roy Davis (*Inocybe*) Massimo Candusso,Alick Henrici, Leif Ryvarden and Mario Tortelli for his many field identification visits to North Cyprus.

Finally, a debt of gratitude must go to my son Kevin Viney and my friend Caroline Hobart whose assistance in proof reading, digitising the text and technical assistance has been essential for the production of this book.

Map of North Cyprus showing collecting area

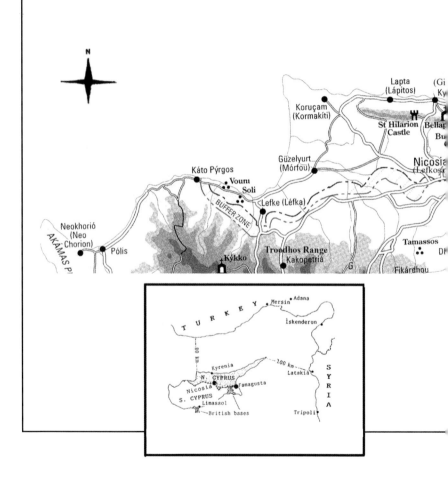

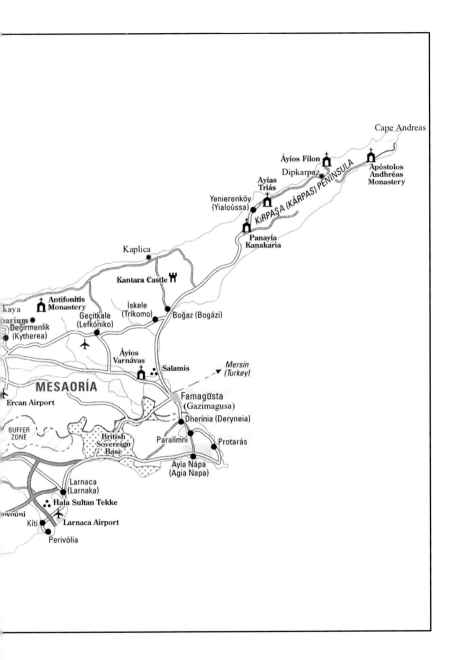

Cape Andreas

Áyios Fílon
Dipkarpaz
Ayías
Triás
Yenierenköy
(Yialoússa)
KIRPAŞA (KÁRPAS) PENINSULA
Apóstolos
Andhréas
Monastery
Panayía
Kanakaria
Kaplica

Kantara Castle

kaya
Antifonítis
Monastery
İskele
(Tríkomo)
Boğaz (Bogázi)
barium
Degirmenlik
(Kytherea)
Geçitkale
(Lefkóniko)

Áyios
Varnávas
Salamis
Mersin
(Turkey)
MESAORÍA
Ercan Airport
Famagusta
(Gazimagusa)
Dherínia (Deryneia)
BUFFER
ZONE
British
Sovereign
Base
Paralímni
Protarás
Ayía Nápa
(Agia Napa)
Larnaca
(Larnaka)
Hala Sultan Tekke
ovoúni
Kíti
Larnaca Airport
Perivólia

GREEK–TURKISH PLACE NAME EQUIVALENTS

Greek	Turkish	Greek	Turkish
Aghirda	Ağırdağ	Kythrea	Değirmenlik
Akanthou	Tatlısu	Lapathos	Boğaziçi
Angastina	Aslanköy	Lapithos	Lapta
Ardhana	Ardahan	Larnaka tis Lapithou	Kozan
Asomatos	Özhan	Lefka	Lefke
Ayia Irini	Akendiz	Lefkoniko	Geçitkale
Ayios Amvrosios	Esentepe	Leonarisso	Ziyamet
Ayios Andronikos (Trikomo)	Topçuköy	Liveras	Sadrazamköy
Ayios Andronikos (Yialousa)	Yeşilköy	Louroujina	Akıncılar
Ayios Epiktitos	Çatalköy	Melounda	Mallıdağ
Ayios Seryios	Yenboğaziçi	Mia milea	Haspolat
Ayios Symeon	Avtepe	Milea	Yıldırım
Ayios Theodoros (Famagusta)	Çayırova	Monarga	Boğaztepe
Ayios Yeoryios (Kyrenia)	Karaoğlanoğlu	Morphou	Güzelyurt
Bellapais	Beylerbeyis	Mousoulita	Kurudere
Boghaz	Boğaz	Myrtou	Çamlibel
Cape Andreas	Zafer Burnu	Nicosia	Lefkoşa
Cape Kormakiti	Koruçam Burnu	Orga	Kayalar
Dhavlos	Kaplıca	Orta Keuy	Ortaköy
Dhioros	Tepebaşı	Ovgoros	Ergazi
Dhikomo	Dikmen	Paleosophos	Malatya
Engomi	Tuzla	Panagra	Geçitköy
Ephtakomi	Yedikonuk	Pendayia	Yeşilyurt
Exometokhi	Düzova	Peristerona (Famagusta)	Alaniçi
Famagusta	Gazimağusa	Perivolia tou Trikomou	Bahçeler
Galatia	Mehmetiçik	Philia	Serhadköy
Galinoporni	Kaleburnu	Phlamoudi	Mersinlik
Gastria	Kalecik	Phterykha	Ilgaz
Geunyeli	Gönyeli	Platanisso	Balalan
Gypsos	Akova	Potamos tou Kambou	Yedidalga
Halevga	Alevkayası	Prastio (Famagusta)	Dörtyol
Kalogrea	Bahçeli	Rizokarpasso	Dipkarpaz
Kalokhorio (Morphou)	Kalkanlı	Sisklipos	Akçiçek
Kambyli	Hisarköy	Skylloura	Yılmazköy
Kanli	Kanlıköy	Strongylos	Türünçlü
Karakoumi	Karakum	Styllos	Mutluyaka
Karavas	Alsancak	Syngrasis	Sınırüstü
Karavostasi	Gemikonağı	Syrianokhori	Yayla
Karmi	Karaman	Tavros	Pamuklu
Kazaphani	Ozanköy	Temblos	Zeytinlik
Kharcha	Karaağaç	Thermia	Doğanköy
Klepini	Arapköy	Trikomo	Iskele
Knodhara	Gönendere	Trimithi	Edremit
Koemuercue	Kömürcü	Tymbou	Kırklar
Koma tou Yialou	Kumyalı	Varosha	Maraş
Komi Kebir	Büyükkonuk	Vasili	Gelincik
Kormakiti	Koruçam	Vasilia	Karşıyaka
Korovia	Kuruova	Vathylakkas	Derince
Kouklia (Famagusta)	Köprülü	Vavilas	Güzelyalı
Koutsovendis	Güngör	Vouno	Taşkent
Krini	Pınarbaşı	Yerani	Turnalar
Kyrenia	Girne	Yerolakkos	Alayköy
		Yialousa	Yenierenköy

TURKISH–GREEK PLACE NAME EQUIVALENTS

Turkish	Greek etc	Turkish	Greek etc
Ağırdağ	Aghirda	Kanlıköy	Kanli
Akçiçek	Sisklipos	Kaplıca	Dhavlos
Akendiz	Ayia Irini	Karaağaç	Kharcha
Akıncılar	Louroujina	Karakum	Karakoumi
Akova	Gypsos	Karaman	Karmi
Alaniçi	Peristerona	Karaoğlanoğlu	Ayios Yeoryios
Alayköy	Yerolakkos	Karşıyaka	Vasilia
Alevkaya (sı)	Halevga	Kayalar	Orga
Alsancak	Karavas	Kırklar	Tymbou
Arapköy	Klepini	Kömürcü	Koemuercue
Ardahan	Ardhana	Köprülü	Kouklia
Aslanköy	Angastina	Koruçam	Kormakiti
Avtepe	Ayios Symeon	Koruçam Burnu	Cape Kormakiti
Bahçeler	Perivolia tou Trikomou	Kozan	Larnaka tis Lapithou
Bahçeli	Kalogrea	Kumyalı	Koma tou Yialou
Balalan	Platanisso	Kurudere	Mousoulita
Beylerbeyis	Bellapais	Kuruova	Korovia
Boğaz	Boghaz	Lapta	Lapithos
Boğaziçi	Lapathos	Lefke	Lefka
Boğaztepe	Monarga	Lefkoşa	Nicosia, Lefkosia
Büyükkonuk	Komi Kebir	Malatya	Paleosophos
Çamlibel	Myrtou	Mallıdağ	Melounda
Çatalköy	Ayios Epiktitos	Maraş	Varosha
Çayırova	Ayios Theodoros	Mehmetiçik	Galatia
Değirmenlik	Kythrea	Mersinlik	Phlamoudi
Derince	Vathylakkas	Mutluyaka	Styllos
Dikmen	Dhikomo	Ortaköy	Orta Keuy
Dipkarpaz	Rizokarpasso	Ozanköy	Kazaphani
Doğanköy	Thermia	Özhan	Asomatos
Dörtyol	Prastio	Pamuklu	Tavros
Düzova	Exometokhi	Pınarbaşı	Krini
Edremit	Trimithi	Sadrazamköy	Liveras
Ergazi	Ovgoros	Serhadköy	Philia
Esentepe	Ayios Amvrosios	Sınırüstü	Syngrasis
Gazimağusa	Famagusta	Taşkent	Vouno
Geçitkale	Lefkoniko	Tatlısu	Akanthou
Geçitköy	Panagra	Tepebaşı	Dhioros
Gelincik	Vasili	Topçuköy	Ayios Andronikos
Gemikonağı	Karavostasi	Turnalar	Yerani
Girne	Kyrenia	Türünçlü	Strongylos
Gönendere	Knodhara	Tuzla	Engomi
Gönyeli	Geunyeli	Yayla	Syrianokhori
Güngör	Koutsovendis	Yedidalga	Potamos tou Kambou
Güzelyalı	Vavilas	Yedikonuk	Ephtakomi
Güzelyurt	Morphou	Yenboğaziçi	Ayios Seryios
Haspolat	Mia milea	Yenierenköy	Yialousa
Hisarköy	Kambyli	Yeşilköy	Ayios Andronikos
Ilgaz	Phterykha	Yeşilyurt	Pendayia
Iskele	Trikomo	Yıldırım	Milea
Kaleburnu	Galinoporni	Yılmazköy	Skylloura
Kalecik	Gastria	Zafer Burnu	Cape Andreas
Kalkanlı	Kalokhorio	Zeytinlik	Temblos
		Ziyamet	Leonarisso

9

Abbreviations and Glossary

Asci	Plural of ascus	aff	Close to
Adnate	Gills joined completely to stem	Fr.	French
Adnexed	Gills partially joined to stem	Ger.	German
Basidia	Plural of basidium	Gk	Greek
Clitocyboid	Like a Clitocybe see page 20	incl	including
Cortina	Veil made of filaments	Lat	Latin
Decurrent	Gills sloping like a funnel down stem	subsp	subspecies
Free	Gills not attached to stem	TRNC	Turkish Republic
of			North Cyprus
Genera	Plural of genus		
Genus	Group of similar fungi	var.	variety
Hygrophanous	Colour changes with humidity	mm	millimetre
Hymenium	A layer of fertile cells	±	more or less
Hyphae	Threads of fungal cells		
Inocyboid	Like an Inocybe see page 20		
Mycenoid	Like a Mycena see page 20		
Mycorrhizal	The symbiotic relationship between a plant and a fungus		
Septate	Wall like separation in cell		
Sinuate	Curved attachment of gill to stem		
Sterigmata	Spore bearing prongs at top of basidium		
Trichalomatoid	Like a Tricholoma see page 20		
Umbonate	Central dome on cap		
Volva	Remains of encompassing egg like bag found on cap and around base of stipe.		

Selected Bibliography

Bon M.(1987) The Mushrooms and Toadstools of Britain and North-Western Europe. Hodder & Stoughton.

Courtecuisse R. (1995) Mushrooms and Toadstools of Britain and Europe. HarperCollins.

Moser M. (1983) Keys to Agarics and Boleti (Polyporales, Boletales, Agaricales, Russulales) English Translation Roger Phillips Gustav Fisher Verlag.

Phillips R. (1981) Mushrooms and other fungi of Great Britain & Europe. Pan Books Ltd.

Stangl von J. (1989) Die Gattung Inocybe in Bayern. Verlag Der Gesellschaft.

Introduction

Mushrooms versus toadstools

What are mushrooms, what are toadstools, and what is the difference between them? Only in the English-speaking world is this distinction made – and it has no scientific basis. Elsewhere they are grouped together as **fungi** – **mantar** in Turkish. Some of them, or rather their over ground fruit bodies, we know from experience are good to eat, and these are commonly called in Britain "**mushrooms**". Others of similar shape that turn out to be poisonous we call "**toadstools**". But how can we be sure?

There is no rule of thumb. Stories that the good ones can be more easily peeled, or that the bad ones turn a silver spoon black, are old wives tales, and very dangerous ones. The only reliable guide is to get to know your fungi; and the present work tries to help you identify at least a selection of the larger ones that the author has found in North Cyprus. (The South, with its more varied geology and vegetation, has a bigger range.)

If after working through this book you are still not sure which species you have in your hand, play safe and discard it from the kitchen! But take note of its details – colour, shape, smell etc. and the place where you found it – since the information may help further research into a subject, which is only in its infancy in this country. Several kinds popularly thought here to be dangerous are perfectly edible – see the section "Edible or Poisonous?" below.

Fungi in General

We have been careful to call this book an "introduction", for fungi are unpredictable things, their fruit-bodies appearing one year and then perhaps not for several seasons, according to weather and other factors. So, any reader who keeps watching from year to year is likely, and in due course certain, to find species not even shown in the following pages because the author did not have the good luck to see them.

Whereas the writer's two volumes on the *Flora of North Cyprus* have tried to cover all the flowering plants of the country, this one can make no similar claim. There are just too many fungi, and their identification is too unsure.

The fungi are indeed now recognised as a separate kingdom of living things alongside the fauna (animals), the flora (plants, including ferns, mosses and algae) and at least two others comprising single-celled organisms. The fungi include not just the few hundred "mushrooms and toadstools" but the far more numerous moulds, smuts, rusts, yeasts and many other groups, mostly microscopically small but important agents of natural decay. Without them, we should soon be up to our necks in fallen leaves, pine litter and rubbish.

So, what we are looking at in this book are the minority of fungi whose fruit-bodies are large enough to hold in the hand, sometimes called "macrofungi" though there is no strict definition of these.

How to use this book

Since pictures are easier for the beginner to remember, many readers will be tempted to begin by flipping through the whole central part of the book, with illustrations and descriptions on facing pages, in the hope of spotting the kind he is holding. But he should read this **Introduction** first for background information (including a list of edible and poisonous fungi) and then, as he gains experience, go through the **Key**, which follows it. With the help of the **Glossary** of technical words – we have kept these to a minimum, but some are indispensable – he will thus, by answering a series of questions about the appearance of his specimen, be led to the small group or **genus** that it belongs to. The attached **genus number** (*not* page number) and letter will then lead him to the corresponding descriptions and illustrations of the species, or series of species, concerned. (Sometimes also to a related genus sharing the same number, but with different letters.)

Names and Classification of Fungi

Very few fungi have English names, and still fewer Turkish. So the budding fungus student or "mycologist" must accept the fact that the only really established names are the scientific ones in Latin or Latinised (old) Greek. The two-name format prescribed long ago by the Swedes Linnaeus (for animals and plants) and Fries (for fungi) consists, like a person's forename and surname but in reverse order, of the generic name (with a capital letter), followed by the specific name of the particular kind. Thus the "edible morel" is, scientifically, *Morchella esculenta*. (Occasionally a finer distinction is indicated by a third name, that of the regional subspecies or of the variety, labelled **subsp.** or **var.**)

If we want to know how closely related, genetically or in evolutionary terms, two different species are, we have to take account of a whole system of wider relationships shown in the classification list after the key. Here we see that related **genera** (the plural of **genus**) are grouped into one **family**, and related **families** into one **order**. At the top of the hierarchy, our fungi are broken down into two subdivisions, the **ascomycetes** and **basidiomycetes**, explained below on p. 14.

In most textbooks, the binomial, is followed by the (usually abbreviated) "authority" whoever originally conferred or changed the scientific names. For brevity, we have omitted these.

Fungal Headaches

It must be admitted that there are several crucial snags in fungus hunting which do not afflict, for example, the botanist in his search for rare flowers. One is that the reliable naming of fungi requires their examination with a high-power microscope. Since we have to assume that most readers here will not have access to one, we have limited our keys and descriptions to "field characters" detectable by the eye (assisted at most by a 10X or 20X hand-lens), by the nose or by the tongue (a scrap cautiously tasted and then spat out!).

But the original identification, by the author or a consultant, has almost always involved the use of microscopes magnifying up to 1000X and of special chemical reagents.

The second difficulty is that so few professional mycologists have explored Cyprus. The only published "check-list" for the mycoflora of the island, by the British plant pathologist Nattrass, dates from 1937 and included a mere fifty or so kinds of **macrofungi**. So, if we now find a "new" fungus, i.e. one not immediately recognisable from European textbooks with their scant coverage of East Mediterranean species, we are bound to wonder if the novelty is merely something perhaps common in Turkey or in Palestine but simply never described before. Or it might even be peculiar to Cyprus – though that would be surprising since the ranges of individual species, with their tiny wind-blown spores, are on the whole larger than those of the flowering plants that are so often "endemic" to small islands or mountain sites. In short most, if not all of our fungi here are known in Turkey too, and a large proportion in Europe, even in Britain.

A third difficulty lies in fungal classification or "taxonomy" itself. Though the use of Latin binomials is intended to ensure simplicity and permanence, the sad fact is that further research often persuades this or that specialist that a given species should be transferred from genus A to an existing genus B, or to a new genus C. So one fungus may have several names, and we have often had to mention two or more "synonyms" in the text.

The rule is to accept the most recently published name. But whereas one good "flora", and one good botanist, may suffice for the identification of all the flowering plants in one country, for fungi even in little North Cyprus, we may need to consult a different specialist for each genus! This is particularly true of some of the "critical" genera, such as *Mycena, Psathyrella, Inocybe* and *Melanoleuca*. Where doubt remains, we have simply baptized a fungus as, say, *Psathyrella* sp., i.e. as some unknown species of that genus. Or we have used the abbreviation "aff." To denote that it is "close to" some named species.

In these days of DNA research doubts can even arise as to whether a genus, which has traditionally been assigned to one family or order may not, despite appearances, really belong to another. It is already accepted, for example, that the gilled genus *Paxillus* is closer to the pore-bearing *Boletus* than to gill-capped *Tricholoma*.

Finally, we have the headache caused by the unpredictability of fungi themselves, or rather of their fruit-bodies, the only part we normally see. The permanent mycelium or network of minute threads, the hyphae, which constitute the bulk of every fungus, is ever present in the soil, or below the bark of a host-tree and so on, but only in special conditions of weather etc. does a conspicuous fruitbody, or a clump of them, arise. And sometimes these do not deign to appear for several seasons.

The Life History of a Fungus

A fungus is disseminated by spores – objects far smaller than the seeds of a plant, and normally one-celled. They are produced in the fruit-body's **hymenium** of fertile, spore bearing cells in amongst the "ball" of a puffball, forming a layer on the gill-edges of an "agaric" or tube sides of a "bolete".After dispersal and germination, they give rise to thread-like **hyphae**.When two such threads, of different "mating types", meet in favourable conditions, they combine to produce an egg like primordium that leads to a new fruitbody – mushroom shape, club shaped, crust-like or whatever. Most of this fruitbody is a compact tissue of hyphae, but part of it is the hymenium of fertile cells from which the spores of the next generation are released.

The above is a very simplified account. In addition to the sexually produced spores some fungi, for example, produce asexual spores too.Among the macrofungi that we shall describe there are two groups, as we have mentioned; among the **ascomycetes** the spores are produced, usually eight at a time, in tiny sausage-shaped **asci** inside or on the outer surface of the fruitbody, while among the **basidiomycetes**, including all the conventionally shaped "mushrooms", the fertile cells or **basidia** end in two or four prongs called **sterigmata** carrying one spore each outside the cell and finally propelling it on its way to start a new life – if it is lucky.

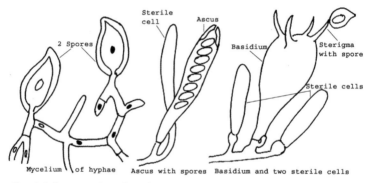

Mycelium of hyphae   Ascus with spores   Basidium and two sterile cells

Crucial features for identifying many basidiomycete fungi (such as the commercial mushroom) are woolly cap-patches, a collar or ring on the stem, and a volva or sac around the stem base.These all arise from two kinds of veil, universal and partial, surrounding the fruit-body from the start.

We illustrate three patterns of development.

    A.   The universal veil ruptures, leaving veil remnants on the cap and a volva at the base.

    B.   There is only a partial veil joining cap margin to stem (sometimes as a web like cortina), rupturing to leave fragments on the cap-margin and or collar, ring or more vaguely a ring zone often stained by falling spores.

    C.   The universal veil remains attached both to the cap and to the lower part of the stem, which is thus enclosed in a sheath.

14

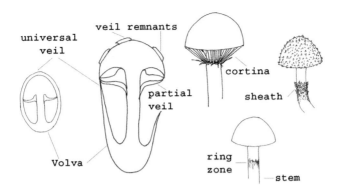

universal veil · veil remnants · cortina · partial veil · sheath · Volva · ring zone · stem

Fungi differ greatly in their life-styles. Unlike plants, they cannot make their own nutrients (like starch and sugar) out of carbon dioxide and water, since they lack the chlorophyll needed for synthesising them – and hence are rarely green. (The green colour of lichens is due to the algae living in partnership with most "lichenised fungi".) Nor can they simply capture and digest them, like animals. Instead, they absorb them.

To do this they adopt one of three strategies. They may be parasitic on living plants or animals, which they may or may not kill; they may be saprophytic on dead animals or vegetation; or they may enjoy a mycorrhizal association benefiting both partners, the fungus forming a web of hyphae round the root-tips of plants through which an exchange of nutrients ensues. This is the case with many large forest fungi, which are selective about the tree-species they partner with.

Problems of Identification: What to notice

These problems start the moment you see a fungus, or even before setting off on a collecting foray. A cardboard or wickerwork basket with compartments is best, a plastic bag (in which fungi sweat) is worst. A stout knife and magnifying glass are desirable, plus (if you are getting serious) a textbook, camera, notebook and pencil. Use the knife to dig up whole fruit-bodies, complete with volva if any, and avoid touching more than necessary. But do slice a complete fruit-body in halves to note any colour changes. Taste (and spit out) a tiny morsel, smell thoughtfully and notice on what and under what the fungus grew. Write these details down; they are soon forgotten and confused on a good day.

The cap-colour might seem too obvious to forget, but it is important to notice changes in colour such as a paling from the centre outwards; species showing this are called **hygrophanous**. Equally critical is any greasiness or stickiness in the cap, and in the stem. The colour of the gills is often "diagnostic" and usually falls into one of five categories: white- to- ochre, pink or pinkish grey, dull ("snuff" or "cigar") brown, bright rusty brown, or purple-to-black. (Beware of immature specimens, where the gill colour may be lighter than unripe ones.)

15

As for spore colour, this may or may not be the same as the gill colour. Since spores are seldom individually visible, and it is the colour of the spores *en masse* that matters, it is essential to take a spore – print as soon as you get home. This is done by placing a whole or half-cap, gills or tubes downward, over a microscope slide or piece of white or white-and-black paper, and covering with a tumbler (after putting a single drop of water on the upper side of the cap). Next morning, or earlier, you will find a neat copy of the gill or tube-pattern on the slide or paper, and there will be no difficulty deciding the true colour.

Edible or Poisonous?

Edible species widely sold in North Cyprus are few:

55 Agaricus bisporus (commercial mushroom, Turk. *Şampinyon*) and several others of the genus, all edible but read the descriptions first!

10 Pleurotus ostreatus var. ferulae, the "Cypriot Oyster Mushroom" (Turk. *Gavçar mantara*) with a very long fruiting season, much sold by children on roadsides; grows in association with the giant Fennel plant.

83a Lactarius deliciosus, the "Saffron Milk-cap" (Turk. *Dağ mantar*), with a very short season in most years, sometimes none; grows under pine trees and *Pistachio lentiniculus*. Prized throughout Europe. When injured it "bleeds" a characteristic carrot-coloured juice, unlike the white or colourless juice of other, inedible, sometimes bitter species.

Edible specic₃ not widely known, but recommended for cooking, are

01 Morchella sp., **Morels** all species. Rare except after fires.

32b,c Tricholoma terreum and *T. portentosum* Only the first named is common, the second is very good, but rare.

33 Lepista nuda the "Wood Blewit", prized in Europe and unmistakable with its blue flushed stem and gills when young. Frequent under pines in some years.

46 Volvariella gloicephala recognised by its slimy cap with no veil remnants (pale in dry weather, dark after rain); no ring but a very evident, torn volva at the stem base. Quite common in grass in December.

57b Coprinus comatus, "Shaggy Inkcap" or "Lawyer's Wig", a distinctive fungus, good if eaten before the gills blacken and liquefy.

There are several large, all white, gill mushrooms (*45a*, *52* and *53*) which are highly tempting but cannot be confidently recommended because some authorities pronounce them edible and others not. And the smaller all-white "Miller", *48p Clitopilus prunulus* indisputably edible, is too rare to be listed here, as are the "edible – when – young" (and well cooked) brackets *15 Laetiporous sulfureus*, "Chicken Of The Woods", and *19b Grifola frondosa*.

Definitely poisonous species are few in this country, though there are many unpalatable ones bitter, tough, slimy or evil smelling and many (like most of the genus), *39 Mycena* too tiny to bother with. In many cases, again, as with the genera *29 Clitocybe* and *68 Inocybe* the difficulty of being sure which species one has found makes it unwise to risk ones luck. Their edibility is largely unknown. In the big genera *50 Lepiota* and *69 Cortinarius* there are, again, some notoriously dangerous kinds, so it is better to avoid them all, just as we naturally avoid the single toxic species of *74 Omphalotus* the attractive "Jack O'lantern", and the equally handsome but uncertainly edible *81 Chroogomphus rutilus*.

European connoisseurs lament the scarcity here of the easily recognized genera *77 Boletus* and *82 Russula*, both with many edible representatives. There are no doubt more of these in the broad-leaved forests of the south. But since they are so rare in the north, they should be left ungathered if only for reason of conservation.

GENERIC KEY TO THE LARGER FUNGI OF NORTH CYPRUS

Choosing between each of two (or more) alternatives after the same left hand number will lead on the right hand either

    a. to the number of the next pair (or more) of alternatives, or
    b. to the relevant genus or genera, whose position(s) in the main illustrated text can then be found in the Index at the end of the book, or sometimes
    c. to a Subkey (A, B or C) with its own sequence of numbers at the end of this key.

1 Cap-and-stem fungus, the usual "mushroom" or "toadstool" shape   2
1 Fungus / fruitbody of some other shape or consistency   4

    2 Only underside of cap fertile (yielding spores), with radiating
       gills or tiny pores or spines   7
    2 Upper side or outside of the variously shaped cap is fertile   3

3a Cap saddle-shaped (see illustrations opposite)   *Helvella*
3b Cap spherical like a small puffball on a tiny stalk   *Tulostoma*
3c Cap on large woody stalk, yielding copious orange spores   *Battarraea*
3d Cap domed and containing granules; on a soft stalk   *Pisolothus*
3e Cap honeycomb patterned, pleasant-smelling   *Morchella*
3f Cap viscid, foul-smelling, later honeycomb patterned   *Phallus*
3g Cap cage-like; stem of several columns   *Colus*

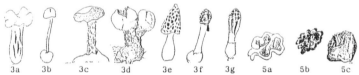

3a   3b   3c   3d   3e   3f   3g   5a   5b   5c

4 No distinct cap-and-stem; fungus jelly-like   5
4 No distinct cap-and-stem; fungus not jelly like; shape various
    but no gills   6

5a Fruitbody bright yellow   *Tremella*
5b Fruitbody almost black, brain-like   *Exidia*
5c Fruitbody brown-to-orange, ear-like   *Auricularia*

    6a Fruitbody club-shaped, ± unbranched   *Clavaria*
    6b Fruitbody coral-shaped, much branched   *Clavulina*
    6c Fruitbody round, very hard and black   *Daldinia*
    6d Fruitbody round, soft, opening at the top with age
       and developing down turned "legs" (earthstar)   *Geastrum*
    6e Fruitbody likewise but without "legless" (puffball) *Vascellum, Lycoperdon*

6f Fruitbody roundish, tough, not opening at the top   *Rhizopogon*
                                                          or *Scleroderma*
6g Fruitbody cup-shaped with marginal lobes   *Cyathus*
6h Fruitbody cup-shaped without marginal lobes   *Peziza, Geopyxis*
6i Fruitbody crust or bracket-like on tree, stump or cut timber   30
6k Fruitbody causing malformation of maize (corn)   *Ustilago*

6a   6b   6c   6d   6e   6f   6h   6i   6j

7a Cap underside with radiating gills (if gills are black and wavy,
   cf sand-loving *Montagnea)*   8
7b Cap underside with tubes, opening through tiny pores
   (but pores sometimes elongated, cf *Gloeophyllum* 35)   28
7c Cap underside with spines   *Sarcodon*

7a   7b

FUNGI with CAP and GILLS (with or without STEM)

8b   9a   9b

8 Stem off-centre or nil   9
8 Stem central under cap (8b)   14

  9 Stem nil (9a)   10
  9 Stem supporting cap at one side (9b)   12

10 Upper side smooth or gelatinous   *Crepidotus*
10 Upper side felty   11

  11 Upper side greyish white, maturing gills split   *Schizophyllum*
  11 Upper side brownish, gills not split   *Gloeophyllum*

12 Gills orange   *Omphalotus,* or *Paxillus panuoides*
12 Gills whitish   13

  13 Cap margin rolled under   *Pleurotus*
  13 Cap margin flat   *Hohenbuehelia*

19

14 Gills wide-spaced, waxy to the touch, spores white   *HYGROPHORACEAE*
14 Gills close or, if wider-spaced, stiff, fragile to the touch   15

   15 Flesh of cap and stem crumbly; all large species   16
   15 Flesh fibrous or elastic, not crumbly; large or small species   17

16 Gills often forked or partially so; no juice exuded when broken   *Russula*
16 Gills usually unforked, continuous from stem to cap-edge;
   almost always exuding juice when broken   *Lactarius*

   17 Gills sloping toward stem or running down it (decurrent)
      giving a."Clitocyboid outline".   18
   17 Gills entirely free (so stem SEPARABLE without damaging gills)   22
   17 Gills more or less horizontal, neither decurrent nor free   28

Types of gill attachment:

free   adnate   adnexed   sinuate   decurrent

Types of outline:

clitocyboid   tricholomatoid   collybioid   mycenoid   inocyboid

Cap and stem fungi with Clitocybe-like outline (gills decurrent)

18 Spore print white or pale ochre   19
18 Spore print pink to brick -red   *Clitopilus*
18 Spore print blackish   *Chroogomphus*

   19 Medium-to-large spp   20
   19 Small slender fungi with bright yellow gills   *Omphalina*

20 Stem with ring   *Armillaria*
20 Stem without ring   21

   21 Gills sharp-edged, whitish   *Ripartites* or *Clitocybe*
   21 Gills fold-like, grey   *Faerbaria*
   21 Gills brown-violaceous   *Psilocybe*

Cap and stem fungi with stem easily separable (since gills free)

22 Stem with a volva (bag) at the base   23
22 Stem without a volva   25

    23 Spore print white   24
    23 Spore print pink   *Pluteus, Volvariella*
    (see also *Entoloma*)

24 Cap glutinous   *Limacella*
24 Cap not glutinous   *Amanita*

    25 Stem with a ring, and sheath below it   *Cystolepiota, Macrolepiota*
    25 Stem with ring or not, but no sheath below it   26

26 Spore print pale to reddish brown   *Bolbitius*
26 Spore print blackish   27

    27 Thick-fleshed fungus like a commercial "mushroom"   *Agaricus*
    27 Thin-fleshed species, gills usually turning into black "ink"   *Coprinus*

Cap and stem fungi with stem not easily separable (since gills not free)
See typical outlines shown on previous page

28 Fleshy cap ± convex, often with raised central umbo:
    (***Tricholoma***-like outline)   **Subkey A below**
28 Cap thin, i.e. less than ¼ its diam., flat or with low umbo:
    (***Collybia***-like outline)   **Subkey B below**
28 Cap thin, hemispherical or bell-shaped (***Mycena***-like outline), or conical
    and, if later flattening, still with sharp umbo (***Inocybe***-like outline)
                          Subkey C below

Cap underside bearing not gills, but tubes opening through pores

29 Tubes separable with thumb from cap-flesh   *BOLETACEAE*
29 Tubes not easily separable from cap-flesh   30

    30 Stem central, flesh elastic   *Polyporus*
    30 Stem little or nil, fruitbody a crust or projecting bracket   31

Crust frond and bracket fungi

31 Fruitbody spread flat over the substrate (bark etc.),
    sometimes with portions curled back   32
31 Fruitbody projecting from the substrate as one or more brackets   33

32 Fruitbody a thin white crust over bark, sometime folded back
Skeletocutis
32 Fruitbody a long off-white firmly attached mass   *Phellinus punctatus*
32 Fruitbody forming separate brown-and white patches on wood
Byssomerulius

33 Fruitbody a branched bouquet of fragile fronds   *Grifola*
33 Fruitbody in an irregular mass, of soft yellow brackets   *Laetiporus*
33 Fruitbody a single projecting bracket, or several joined   34

34 Undersides of fruit-bodies with elongated gill like pores   *Gloeophyllum*
34 Fertile surfaces with roundish pores, often minute   35

35 Bracket(s) less than 1cm thick   36
35 Bracket(s) more than 1cm thick   37

36 Undersides of brackets uniform grey   *Bjerkandera*
36 Undersides pale clay colour   *Trametes*
36 Undersides orange-yellow, upper side hairy   *Stereum*

37 Fungus whitish, brackets joined in vertical series   *Antrodia*
37 Brackets darker, not in vertical series   38

38 Upper surface(s) blackish, flesh woody   *Phellinus*
38 Upper surface(s) brown to orange, flesh corky   39

39 Underside pores small, 4-6 per mm   *Ganoderma*
39 Pores larger, 1-2 per mm   *Coriolopsis*

Subkey A. Cap-and-stem fungi with Tricholoma-like outline

1 Spores white-to-pale   2
1 Spores pink   *Rhodocybe, Clitopilus*
1 Spores brown   7
1 Spores blackish   10

2 Stem with ring, no sheath below   *Leucoagaricus, Sericeomyces*
2 Stem with sheath in lower part   *Cystoderma*
2 Stem without ring or sheath   3

3 Several stems arising from one point   *Lyophyllum*
3 Stems arising singly   4
4 Stem with bluish tones   *Lepista*
4 Stem without bluish tones   5

5 Gills with red or yellow tones   *Rugosomyces*
5 Gills with no red or yellow tones   6

22

6 Cap rather flat with depression between disc and outer zone

Melanoleuca

6 Cap convex with centre-disc the highest point   *Tricholoma*

7 Spore print rusty brown   8
7 Spore print dull tobacco brown   9

  8 Stipe with sheath below ring-zone   *Pholiota*
  8 Stipe with no sheath below ring-zone   *Cortinarius*

9 Cap fibrous, fleecy or scaly   *Inocybe*
9 Cap smooth   *Agrocybe*

  10 Stipe with a ring   *Stropharia*
  10 Stipe with cortina when young, but no ring   *Lacrymaria*

Subkey B Cap-and-stem fungi with Collybia-like outline

1 Spore print white-to-pale   2
1 Spore print pink   *Entoloma*
1 Spore print ochre-to-brown   7
1 Spore print violaceous-to-blackish   8

  2 Stem with a mealy sheath round lower part   *Cystoderma*
  2 Stem with no such sheath   3

3 Smells of rotting cabbage   *Micromphale*
3 No such smell   4

  4 Stem brittle   *Mycena*
  4 Stem tough or elastic   5

5 Cap under 1.5cm in diameter, shaggy   *Crinipellis*
5 Cap 2-5cm in diameter, smooth   6

  6 Stem tough, not snapping when twisted   *Marasmius*
  6 Stem elastic but splitting when twisted   *Collybia*

7 Spore print rust-coloured   *Tubaria*
7 Spore print dull brown   *Cortinarius*

  8 Stem with a ring   *Stropharia*
  8 Stem without a ring   *Psathyrella*

Subkey C Cap-and-stem fungi with Mycena or Inocybe-like outline

1 Spore print white-to-pale	*Mycena*
1 Spore print pink	*Entoloma*
1 Spore print ochre-to-brown	2
1 Spore print blackish	4
2 Cap thin-fleshed, often striate	3
2 Cap fleshier, often fibrous but not striate	*Inocybe*
3 Cap apex convex	*Galerina*
3 Cap apex ± acute, conical	*Conocybe*
4 Gills grey-black mottled, not deliquescing into "ink"	*Panaeolus*
4 Gills not grey-black mottled, sometimes "deliquescing"	5

5 Gills blackening from edge upwards, usually deliquescing into "ink"
Coprinus
5 Gills maturing uniformly dark but never deliquescing   *Psathyrella*

Classification of species described

In this list all the macrofungi observed in North Cyprus to date are arranged by **Subdivision** (ending in -ina), **Order** (-ales), **Family** (-aceae), **Genus** (capitalised) and species, occasionally also by variety, according to the sequence followed in the mycology department at Kew. For simplicity, "citation authorities" – abbreviations given after the scientific names in advanced textbooks, to show who in each case first conferred these names – have been omitted. Under the long accepted "binominal" system, the genus and species (and sometimes variety) suffice to name a particular fungus as they do a plant or animal. Where names have been changed in the course of research, **synonyms,** which the reader may find in other books, have sometimes been mentioned in the main text, at the start of the species description.

These descriptions, and the illustrations on facing pages, can be located through the systematic **Genus Number** and **Species Letter** (where there is more than one species) given after each name below. The index at the back of the book likewise gives, not the page number, but the systematic number used for the whole Genus to which the fungus under investigation belongs, or sometimes to a related Genus also, but then with a distinguishing letter after the number.

*Indicates approximate or tentative identification.

**Indicates species not recorded in N. Cyprus – but see text.

SUBDIVISION ASCOMYCOTINA
Order **Pezizales**
 Family **Morchellaceae**
  Morchella esculenta 01a
  M. elata 01b
 Family **Helvellaceae**
  Helvella lacunosa 02
 Family **Pezizaceae**
  Sarcosphaera crassa 03
  Peziza ampelina 04a
  P. limnaea 04b
  P. vesiculosa 04c
  P. violacea 04d
  Plicaria leiocarpa 05
  Geopyxis carbonaria 06
  Melastiza chateri 06x

Order **Xylariales**
 Family **Xylariaceae**
  Daldinia concentrica 07

SUBDIVISION BASIDIOMYCOTINA
Order **Cantherellales**
 Family **Clavariaceae**
  Clavaria incarnata 08
  Clavulina cristata 09

Order **Poriales**
 Family **Lentinaceae**
  Pleurotus eryngii 10
  Lentinus conchatus 11
  Faerbaria carbonaria 12
 Family Polyporaceae
  Polyporus meridionalis 13
  Trametes pubescens 14a
  T. versicolor 14b
  Laetiporus sulphureus
 Family **Coriolaceae**
  Antrodia serialis 16
  Coriolopsis gallica 17
  Gloeophyllum abietinum 18a
  G. trabeum 18b
  Bjerkandera adusta 19a
  Grifola frondosa 19b
  Skeletocutis nivea 19c
Order **Ganodermatales**
 Family **Ganodermataceae**
  Ganoderma adspersum 20

Order **Hymenochaetales**
 Family **Hymenochaetaceae**
  Phellinus igniarius 21a
  P. punctatus 21d
  P. rimosus 21c
  P. torulosus 21b
  Phylloporia ribis 21r

Order **Stereales**
 Family **Stereaceae**
  Stereum hirsutum 22
 Family **Meruliaceae**
  Byssomerulius corium 23
  Schizophyllum commune 24
 Family **Thelephoraceae**
  Sarcodon sp 24x*

Order **Agaricales**
 Family **Hygrophoraceae**
  Hygrophorus carneogriseus 25b
  H. latitabundus 25a
  Hygrocybe chlorophana 26a*
  H. conica 26b
  Cuphophyllus virgineus 27
 Family **Tricholomataceae**
  Lyophyllum decastes 28a
  L. sp. 28b*
  Clitocybe alexandri 29b
  C. augeana 29j
  C. candicans 29f
  C. costata 29a
  C. diatreta 29e
  C. ditopus 29d
  C. inversa 29h
  C. obsoleta 29c
  C. umbilicata 29g
  C. vermicularis 29i
  Armillaria mellea 30
  Omphalina sp. 31*
  Tricholoma fracticum 32a
  T. portentosum 32c
  T. terreum 32b
  Lepista nuda 33
  Myxomphalia maura 34
  Collybia dryophila 35
  Marasmius rotula 36a
  M. anomalus 36b
  M. wynneae 36c

Crinipellis scabella 37
Micromphale brassicolens 38
Mycena amicta 39b
M. galopus 39a
M. oortiana 39c
M. pura 39 f
M. sanguinolenta 39d
M. seynesii 39e
Xeromphalina fellea 40
Melanoleuca brevipes 41c
M. excissa 41a, d
M. paedida 41b
M. rasilis var. rasilis 41e
Rugosomyces chrysenteron 42a
R. onychinus 42b
Hohenbuehelia geogenia 43
Family **Amanitaceae**
  Limacella illinita 44a
  *Amanita malleata** 45c
  *A. muscaria*** 45e
  A. ovoidea 45a
  *A. phalloides***45d
  *A. proxima** 45b
Family **Pluteaceae**
  Volariella gloiocephala 46
  *Pluteus cinereofuscus** 47
Family **Entolomataceae**
  *Entoloma hirtipes** 48a
  E. jubatum 48c
  E. phaeocyathum 48d
  E. undatum 48b
  Clitopilus prunulus 48p
  Rhodocybe popinalis 48r
  R. geminae 48s
Family **Agaricaceae**
  Cystolepiota cystophora 49
  Lepiota castanea 50a
  *L. clypeolaria** 50b
  *L. brunneoincarnata** 50c
  Macrolepiota konradii 51
  Sericeomyces serenus 52
  *Leucoagaricus leucothites** 53
  Chamaemyces fracidus 54
  Agaricus bitorquis 55b
  A. campestris 55a
  A. gennadii 55d
  *A. macrocarpus** 55f
  A. porphyrizon 55c

*A. silvaticus** 55e
Cystoderma amianthinum 56a
C. terreyi 56b
Family **Coprinaceae**
  Coprinus cinereus 57d
  C. comatus 57b
  C. cothurnatus 57f
  C. domesticus 57c
  C. flocculosus 57g
  C. megaspermus 57j
  C. ovatus 57h
  C. picaceus 57a
  C. plicatilis 57e
  *C. xerophilus*see* 57g
  Panaeolus papilionaceus 58a
  Panaeolus olivaceus 58b
  Psathyrella bipellis 59a
  P. candolleana 59c
  P. lacrymabunda 59m
  P. spadiceogrisea 59b
  *Psathyrella sp.** 59d
  *Psathyrella sp.** 59e
Family **Bolbitiaceae**
  Bolbitius tener 60
  Pholiotina filaris 61
  Agrocybe sp. 62
Family **Strophariaceae**
  Pholiota carbonaria 63a
  P. mixta 63b
  Stropharia aeruginosa 64a
  S. coronilla 64b
  Psilocybe crobula 65
Family **Podaxaceae**
  Montagnea hausknechtii 66
  Gyrophragmium dunallii 66a

Order **Cortinariales**
  Family **Cortinariaceae**
    Gymnopilus flavus 67
    *Inocybe bongardii** 68b
    I. dulcamara 68a
    I. flocculosa 68d
    I. grisovelata 68f
    I. lacera 68e
    *I. nitidiuscula** 68h
    I. obscurobadia 68g
    I. pisciodora 68c
    *I. sindonia** 68i

Cortinarius dionysae 69a
Cortinarius sp. 69b
Family **Crepidotaceae**
Galerina marginata 70b
G. vittaeformis 70a
Tubaria autochthona 71a
T. conspersa 71b
T. furfuracea 71c
Crepidotus cesatii 72c
C. mollis 72a
C. variabilis 72b

Order **Boletales**
Family **Rhizopogonaceae**
Rhizopogon luteolus 73a
R. vulgaris 73b
Family **Paxillaceae**
Omphalotus olearius 74
Paxillus panuoides 75
Ripartites tricholoma 76
Family **Boletaceae**
Boletus rhodopurpureus 77
Suillus bellini 78a
S. granulatus 78c
S. mediterraneensis
Xerocomus chrysenteron 79
Chalciporus amarellus 80
Family **Gomphidiaceae**
Gomphidius rutilus 81

Order **Russulales**
Family **Russulaceae**
Russula delica 82c
R. luteotacta 82a
R. sanguinea 82b
R. torulosa 82d
Lactarius deliciosus 83a

Order **Lycoperdales**
Family **Geastraceae**
Geastrum berkeleyi 84c
G. pseudolimbatum 84d
G. sessile 84b
G. triplex 84a

Family **Lycoperdaceae**
Lycoperdon perlatum 85
Vascellum pratense 86
Bovista plumbea 87a
Bovista nigrescens 87b

Order **Tulostomatales**
Family **Tulostomataceae**
Tulostoma squamosum 88
Battarrea stevenii 89

Order **Nidulariales**
Family **Nidulariaceae**
Cyathus olla 90

Order **Sclerodermatales**
Family **Pisolithaceae**
Scleroderma verrucosum 91
Pisolithus arrhizus 92

Order **Phallales**
Family **Phallaceae**
Phallus impudicus 93
Family **Clathraceae**
Colus hirudinosus 94

Order **Tremellales**
Family **Tremellaceae**
Tremella mesenterica 95
Exidia glandulosa 96

Order **Auriculariales**
Family **Auriculariaceae**
Auricularia auricula-judae 97

Order **Ustilaginales**
Family **Ustilaginaceae**
Ustilago zeae 98

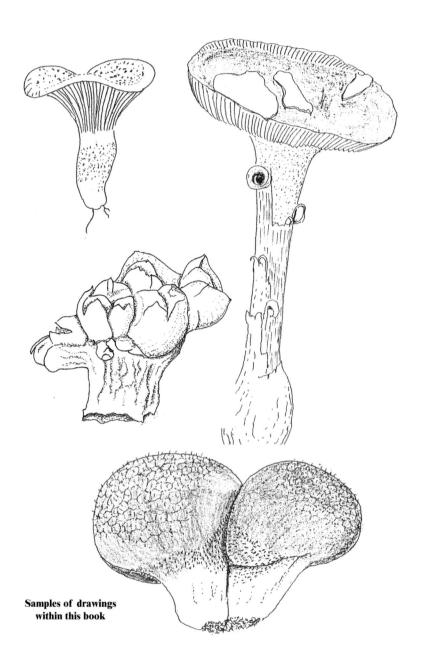

**Samples of drawings
within this book**

28

Illustrations and Descriptions of Species

The "mushrooms and toadstools" dealt with in this book are also loosely called *macrofungi* because they are members of the fungal kingdom big enough to handle. They fall scientifically into two subkingdoms, the Ascomycetes and the Basidiomycetes; the distinction, though crucial, is unfortunately invisible to the naked eye. In the Ascomycetes (of which there are about 150,000 worldwide, though they include only a few of the species pictured here) the reproductive spores – far smaller than the seeds of plants – are formed, usually in rows of 8, each row inside a special cell or **ascus** (plural **asci**). Among the Basidiomycetes, by contrast, the spores develop outside one end of the fertile cell or **basidium** (plural **basidia**), usually on the tips of four prongs or **sterigmata.** See preface above.

Each subkingdom is divided into various orders, each order into one or more families. Each family comprises one **genus** or more (plural **genera**) and each individual kind is a species, sometimes with minor variants termed subspecies or varieties.

Our first two orders, covering five families, include fungi of varied and distinctive shapes, none of them like mushrooms at all.

ASCOMYCETES

Order **PEZIZALES**   Family **MORCHELLACEAE**

Our first genus, **MORCHELLA** (its old Latin name), comprises the several species of "Morel", with distinct stems and honeycomb patterned hollow caps covered with asci (visible only under the microscope) that open at the tips to release the spores. They are all edible (imported dry to the UK) and much prized from Germany to Turkey, but rather rare in Cyprus and little known though they appeared abundantly in some parts of the island after the fire of 1995. We have seen at least two species, the round-headed

01a Morchella esculenta (Lat. "edible"), usually in grass under broad-leaved trees (and on sandy soil near Akdeniz)

01b M. elata (Lat. "tall"). Which is more pointed is usually under pines (Lapta, Karaman), and is often found in groups with several fruit-bodies growing together. Cap colour of both species is variable and is usually grey or beige.

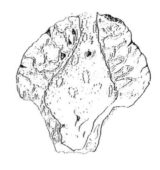

01a Morchella esculenta

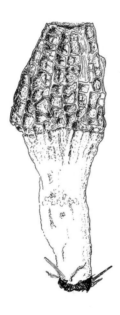

01b Morchella elata

Order **PEZIZALES**   Family **HELVELLACEAE**

The main genus in this family is

Helvella (Lat. "pale brown" but colours vary), whose members have a distinctive saddle-shaped cap. Here we have seen only

02 Helvella lacunosa, typically c.8cm tall with dark ridges and pale furrows (Lat. lacunae, "gaps") up the stem). But pigmy, down to stemless, specimens occur in dry wayside scree e.g. above Lapta. The "saddle" is sooty-black outside, white and pitted on the fertile underside; in damp pinewood nr Alevkaya, Mar.1997

Order **PEZIZALES**   Family **PEZIZACEAE**

This family of largely cup-shaped fungi contains several genera only microscopically distinguishable, including

Sarcosphaera (Gk "fleshy sphere"), represented here by

03 Sarcosphaera crassa (Lat. "thick"), found in pine litter and moss, e.g. nr Alevkaya, initially as a white globe which splits irregularly to reveal a pinkish inner surface carrying the asci.

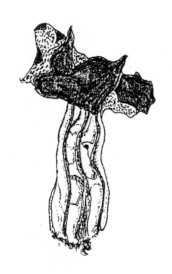

02 *Sarcosphaera crassa*

03 *Sarcosphaera crassa*

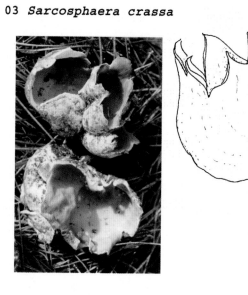
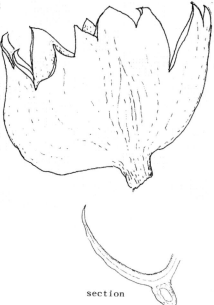

section

Another four allied genera in the same family, all cup-shaped, are **PEZIZA** itself (Gk "growing on the ground"), **PLICARIA** (Lat. "folded") **GEOPYXIS** (Gk "little box on the ground") and **MELASTIZA;** without trying to define them we shall present a few species that have been identified for this country by specialists. There must be many more awaiting patient research.

In the large genus *PEZIZA,* species recorded here include

04a Peziza ampelina (Lat. "vine-leaf coloured"), shallow, with inner and outer surfaces violaceous (the inner darker), edge ± entire; on soil under Cistus above Alsancak Dec. 2001:

04b P. limnaea, (**Gk** "lakeside", an occasional habitat) deeply cup shaped with the outer surface pale, and the inner black when ripe, edge warty: on soil under Cistus nr Kayalar Dec. 2001:

top view

transverse section

04a *Peziza ampelina*

04b *Peziza limnae*

illustrations cont.

04c P. vesiculosa (Lat. "bladder-like"), deep cup-shaped, hazel inside and out, edge finely scalloped, very short stem: in troops in turf above Alsancak Dec. 2001;

04d P. violacea (Lat. "violet" but colour variable), shallow, pale bay, edge scalloped, stem nil; on sandy soil beside Geçitköy reservoir Dec. 2001.

side view

flesh ± 1mm thick

o4c *Peziza vesiculosa*

04d *Peziza violacea*

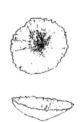

top (inner)
and side view

Order **PEZIZALES** Family **PEZIZACEAE**

The allied genus *Plicaria* distinguished from *Peziza* by spore shape is represented here by

05 Plicaria leiocarpa (Gk "with smooth fruit (body))", shallow, blackish inside and out, wavy-edged, to 2cm in diam.; on sandy soil beside Geçitköy reservoir Dec. 2001

Order **PEZIZALES** Family **OTIDEACEAE**

06 Geopyxis carbonaria (Lat. "associated with charcoal" from growing on burnt ground), cup-shaped with encrusted edge, reddish-orange inside, orange-buff outside; bare soil above Karaman Feb. 1997 on site of 1995 fire.

06x Melastiza chateri, disc shaped and slightly undulating, often growing in large numbers and carpeting the ground; bright orange with short brown tufts surrounding the rim (hand lens); up to 1.5cms in diam. on a quarry floor on the ridge road toward Alevkaya Dec. 2004

06 **Geopyxis carbonara**

life-size

05 **Plicaria leiocarpa**

06x **Melastiza chateri**

39

Our last, very distinctive ascomycete takes us into a new order, **XYLARIALES,** and family **XYLARIACEAE** (appropriately from the Gk for "wood"), whose unmistakable representative here as in Europe is

07 *Daldinia concentrica*. It has two expressive Eng. names: "King Alfred's Cakes" (the legendary burnt offerings) and "Cramp Balls" (from the belief that carried on the person, they protected against rheumatism). The fruitbody is indeed like a woody ball, reddish-brown turning black and hard, showing concentric annual zones when cut, with the black asci forming in the outermost layer and spores being released throughout the year via tiny pores or "ostioles". Grows on various trees, notably ash, in Europe but here found by the writer only once, on the edge of a chipboard table exposed to rain over the winter.

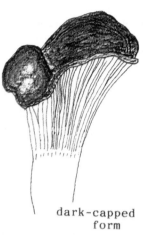

dark-capped
form

10 Pleurotus eryngii var. *ferulae*,
showing *Ferula* host foliage

N. Cyprus stamp
issued Mar. 1997

45

11 Lentinus conchatus (Lat."shell-shaped") (also called ***Panus conchatus***) is another large fungus, up to 12cm across, usually perched on an eccentric stem growing from dead or buried wood. In the case illustrated, the fruitbody was on soil between rocks, but perhaps attached to *Olive* or *Carob* roots above Karşiyaka Jan. 2001.

The flesh is tough and INEDIBLE. Cap and gills start ± lilac and turn yellow-brown.

11 Lentinus conchatus

Order **PORIALES** Family **LENTINACEAE**

Our third genus in the family, *Faerbaria* (after a botanist Faerber), is represented by the rather rare species

12 Faerbaria carbonaria (Lat. "charcoal-loving" from appearing on burnt sites). Cap sooty grey, darker in central depression, splitting when old; gill-like folds under the cap whitish, deeply decurrent; stem glossy, white, aging grey. Found among cinders under pines near the ridge road above St Hilarion, Dec. 2000.

Order **PORIALES** Family **POLYPORACEAE**

This and the following family, unlike the preceding one, release their spores through short tubes instead of gills (or gill-like folds). The genus **Polyporus** (Gk "many pores") has these tubes, ending in pores, on the underside of a cap and so looks more like a conventional mushroom, such as a Bolete, than any other fungus in this order. It is represented here only by

13 Polyporus meridionalis (Lat. "southerly", not known in northern Europe), with slightly zoned light brown cap pattern, tough whitish stem and tubes (that cannot be scraped off the cap) ending in large ± hexagonal pores. Quite common on roots of pine trees and garigue shrubs.

12 Faerbaria carbonaria

marginal part of
spore-bearing
undersurface
magnified 10X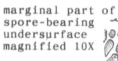

13 Polyporus meridionalis

The next genus, **Trametes** (Gk the "woof" of cloth), is represented here by two "bracket fungi" growing on dead or dying wood.

14a Trametes pubescens forms closely tiered groups of fruit-bodies only a few mm thick; the upper, sterile, surface is buff-coloured and paler towards the edge, the lower, fertile surface, or "hymenium", clay-coloured and covered with tiny pores except for the narrow white edge. The pores open from tubes only 1.2 mm long. Found on an apple stump in Lefke, Feb. 1997.

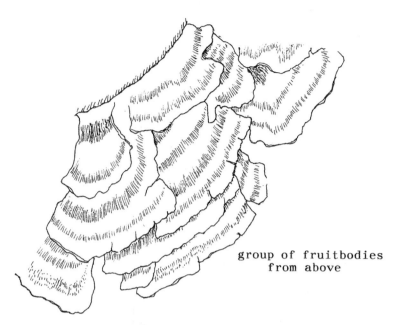

group of fruitbodies
from above

14a Trametes pubescens

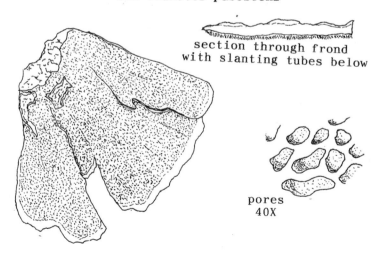

section through frond
with slanting tubes below

pores
40X

Another annual species of the same genus **Trametes** is

14b Trametes versicolor, growing in overlapping groups of tough, fan-shaped, wavy-edged fruit-bodies. The upper surface is concentrically zoned with the outermost zone palest, velvety at first but becoming smooth; the fertile under-surface is cream-coloured, then buff, with small angular pores (2-3 per mm.) at the end of tubes less than 1 mm long. An attractive, but INEDIBLE fungus, like most of the "brackets". Common in Europe on broad-leaved trees, here found on a *Carob* stump above Kozan, Dec. 1998.

In the same family, we have the very distinctive genus ***Laetiporus*** (Lat. "gay" + "pore" from the bright yellow surface), with the single species

15 Laetiporus sulfureus (Lat. "sulphur coloured"). The yellow body expands from a single hump to an array of wavy, round-edged brackets whose fertile surfaces are dotted with pores too small at first to be seen by the naked eye, opening from 4mm long tubes. The flesh is at first bright yellow, then white and crumbly. EDIBLE when young if well cooked, with a taste justifying its English name of "Chicken of the woods".
In Europe, found on various broad-leaved trees, and on *Yew*. Here seen only once, kicked down, on the *Persian lilac **Melia azedarach*** outside the Girne telephone office, Nov. 1999

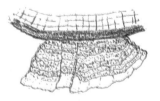

***14b** Trametes versicolor*

fruitbodies
from above

fruitbody
from below

15 Laetiporus sulfureus

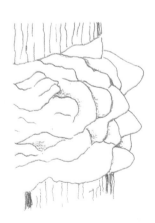

Another family of brackets, some with pores and some with shallow maze-like slots on their undersides. The small genus **Antrodia** is represented here by

16 *Antrodia serialis* (Lat. "in (vertical) rows" like the fruit-bodies), a tough, leathery annual, yellowish-cream outside but with white flesh. It spreads in vertical patches along the fissures of conifer bark – especially *Spruce* in Europe, but pine here (above Karaman, Dec. 1999). It causes "carbonising rot" that turns affected timber dark brown. The tubes, to c.5mm long, end in small round pores that cover most of the brackets; only the upper surfaces are sterile. The whole fungus is easily detached.

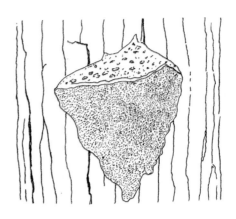

16 Antrodia serialis

pore surface 20X

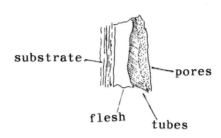

substrate — | — pores

flesh   tubes

A second genus, *Coriolopsis* (Lat./Gk "like soft leather"), is represented here by

17 *Coriolopsis gallica* (Lat. "Gaulish" since first described from France), forming corky brackets, thicker than the preceding and spreading horizontally. Fruit-bodies dark brown and at first hairy above, paler (but darkening) on the lower, fertile surfaces which bear tubes up to 1cm long ending in rather large angular pores, 1-2 per mm. Test: the brown flesh turns black with KOH.

In Europe, it grows mostly on *Ash*; but found here on live *Walnut* and on cut timber, which succumbs to a white-rot where infected.

pores 40X

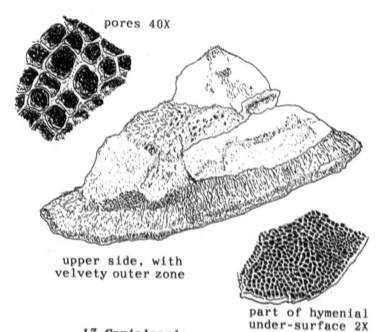

upper side, with
velvety outer zone

part of hymenial
under-surface 2X

*17 Coriolopsis
gallica*

fruitbodies on
live walnut

The genus **GLOEOPHYLLUM** (Gk "sticky gilled"), also termed **LENZITES,** brings us to brackets with maze-like gills, rather than pores, on the fertile under-surface. Two species are found here, both causing brown rot in infected trees.

18a Gloeophyllum abietinum (Lat. A*bies,* one host-tree in Europe).
The brackets are often found here in numbers on the sides and cut surfaces of felled *Cypresses* and pines, while in Europe the *Spruce* is the commonest host. The upper surface is dark brown, hairy and zoned (with the outermost zone paler); flesh dark and rubbery; under surface covered with a labyrinth of false gills, joining up in places, cigar-brown to black with light edges.

In *18b Gloeophyllum trabeum* (Lat. "on planks"), found on dead conifers and sawn wood here, the fertile under surfaces, show some conventional pores (1.2 per mm) at the edges opening from cinnamon-coloured tubes up to 1cm long, but these usually become extended gill-like slots toward the centre. The whole bracket has a much broader, rounded, white edge than in **G. abietinum.**

18a Gloeophyllum abietinum

18b Gloeophyllum trabeum

false gills

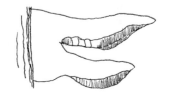

double bracket
in transv. section

extended pores
and gill-like slots

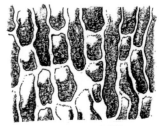

pores 10X

Of the two species of Bjerkandera found in Europe, normally on broadleaved trees only

19a Bjerkandera adusta has been recorded in Cyprus. The specimens shown grew on an unusual substrate, the concrete walls of a manhole near Iskele affording little nutrient or light. The fruit-bodies are groups of thin leathery brackets, brownish and wrinkled above, but a uniform grey on the fertile under-surface. The pores are minute (c.10 per mm), at the ends of the tubes only 1mm long.

Another representative of this family is

19b Grifola frondosa, with numerous fragile tongue-shaped, greyish-brown brackets. Whitish below and 0.5 to 1cm thick with tubes to 3mm long ending in rather large pores. The brackets spring from a repeatedly branched stout stem, the whole resembling a large cabbage up to half a metre across. Found in Europe low down on *Oak* and *Beech* trunks; only one specimen seen in n. Cyprus (nr Yenierenköy) its host tree uncertain. It was promptly eaten by its discoverer and pronounced "good", though European textbooks describe it as edible only when young, otherwise smelling of mice.

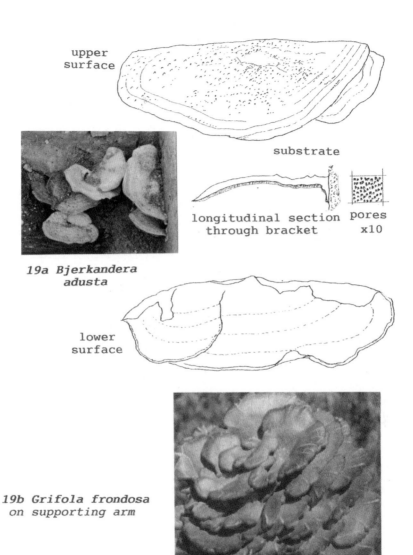

upper
surface

substrate

longitudinal section
through bracket

pores
x10

19a Bjerkandera
adusta

lower
surface

19b Grifola frondosa
on supporting arm

19c Skeletocutis nivea (Gk/Lat. "skeleton- patterned skin") (Lat. "snow white") is an example of the corticoid fungi, whose fruit-bodies stretch like a thin skin (white in this case) over a substrate, e.g. bark, with the pore surface exposed but often curling over to show the sterile under surface too. Here on a dead pine branch; pores shown x15. Common in the woods near Alevkaya.

Order **GANODERMATALES**   Family **GANODERMATACEAE**

The genus *Ganoderma* (Gk "shiny skin") includes some of the most striking (and perennial) bracket fungi, including the "artist's fungus" (*G. applanatum*), so called because one can make a permanent drawing with one's finger-nail on the pale under-surface of a large cap. The species found here is a similar one,

20 Ganoderma adspersum (Lat "sprinkled", because each cap is commonly powdered orange with the spores from the other caps.)
A cross-section (which requires a saw) reveals beneath the knobbly, chestnut skin a tough layer of brown flesh and below it one, or in older fruit-bodies several, annual layers of tubes, each 1 cm or more thick. The tubes end in whitish pores, 4-5 per mm, which bruise dark brown. The only safe distinction between the two species requires a microscope to check the size of the spores (over 12μ long, i.e. 12 thousandths of a mm, in this species but only 8μ in *G. applanatum*).
Both species cause white-rot in the trees they parasitize. In Europe, these include many broadleaved species and conifers too. Here the writer has seen them round a *Fig* stem and on the buried remains of a dead *Almond* (both in Karaman).

pores
x15

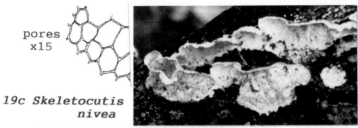

19c *Skeletocutis
nivea*

20 *Ganoderma adspersum (= australe)*
growing round a fig stem

section showing
2 annual tube-layers

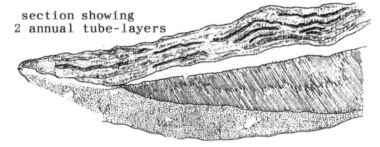

63

The large perennial brackets of the genus ***Phellinus*** have been much subject to name-changes. Various species have been assigned to the genera ***Trametes, Fomes, Ochroporus*** etc. We show four distinctive ones on the following pages.

21a Phellinus igniarius (Lat. "fire-making") is the less effective of two hoof-shaped fungi formerly used to provide tinder for pistols etc. (The other, ***P. fomentarius,*** is softer; not seen here.) The tough fruitbody is firmly attached to a variety of broad-leaved trees, notably *Apple* and *Willow* in Europe, but here found on *Tamarisk* at Ortaköy, Jan. 2001. The upper surface shows concentric bulges, pale to blackish-grey (or even green with algae), the flesh and lower surface are reddish-brown with oblong pores, 2-4 per mm, opening from layered tubes 1-5mm long. The broad margin joining the two surfaces is light grey, darkening to cinnamon.

21a Phellinus igniarius

pore surface

21b P. torulosus (Lat."doughnut-shaped) is another chunky species growing almost inseparably attached to various broad-leaved trees (here, notably *Carob* and *Almond*), with the upper surface blackish, zoned orange-brown but often covered with moss; flesh and pores orange-brown.

21b Phellinus torulosus
fruitbody on base
of carob trunk

fruitbody on
underside of
almond branch
with sterile
surface lowermost

In 21c P. rimosus (Lat."cracked") the black cap cracks when mature into squarish block (found here on a tree-size *Terebinth* at Karaağaç), while

21d P. punctatus (Lat."dotted") differs from the rest in being "resupinate", i.e. the fertile, pore-bearing surface being exposed one. Found here on Olive-stumps and roots (Bellapais, Karaman).

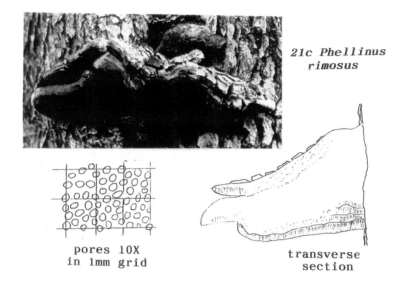

21c *Phellinus rimosus*

pores 10X
in 1mm grid

transverse
section

21d *Phellinus punctatus*

pores 10X

hymenium in section,
c.1mm long

21r Phylloporia ribis (Lat. ribes, "currant" a common host plant). A fungus also called ***Phellinus ribis***, but now separated from that genus because of the distinctive thin dark zone in this species separating the woolly top layer of the cap from the underlying tissue.

The two brackets illustrated (the smaller one inverted to show pore surface) were parasitic on a live *Cistus* branch, but this fungus is recorded in Europe growing on many unrelated trees and shrubs, most commonly on *Euonymus* spp. The cap is dark brown to cinnamon with furrowed concentric zones; the pore surface and tubes (5-6 per mm, pores minute, round-to-angular) are brown, with a yellowish cap-margin. The tissues react black to KOH. It can cause white rot in the host plant. Found in garigue near Kayalar, Dec. 2001

21r *Phylloporia ribis*

With the genus **Stereum** (Gk "solid, firm"), we embark on the difficult territory of crust-like fungi, where the spore-forming surface is quite smooth without pores or gills. In our common species

22 Stereum hirsutum (Lat. "hairy") the fruitbody commonly grows *under* a dead branch, so that the fertile (hymenial) surface is only visible where it curls over. When growing on a vertical substrate however, such as the olive trunk in our photo, it can form very numerous wavy, yellowish brackets, the edges always fringed with hair. Unlike other species in the genus, it does not mark red when scratched.

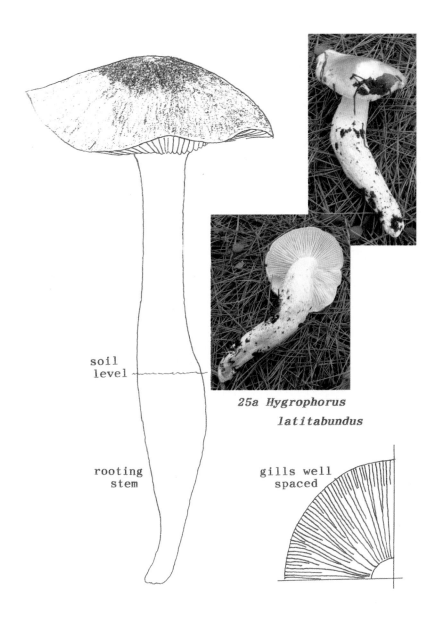

soil
level

25a *Hygrophorus*
    latitabundus

rooting
stem

gills well
spaced

A second Cypriot Waxcap has been tentively named by the Italian fungal specialist Massimo Candusso as the rare

25b Hygrophorus carneogriseus, has a mid-brown cap with in rolled edge, and dirty white stem, both dotted with dark-brown scales, and decurrent beige gills. It has a bitter taste, and smells unpleasantly mealy it is also known from Spain and N. Africa. Found here only on *Cypress* litter by the *Ermeni evi*, below Alevkaya, Jan. 2001.

25b Hygrophorus Carneogriseus

Order **AGARICACEAE**   Family **HYGROPHORACEAE**

Another genus of Waxcaps, *Hygrocybe* (Gk "moist head"), is notable for the bright colours of many species (including our two); they commonly grow as saprophytes in grass, instead of in mycorhizal association with trees like the previous genus.

26a Hygrocybe aff. chlorophana. The orange-yellow fungus shown here astonished foresters when it appeared in numbers in 1999, in grassy patches near Esentepe and Bahçeli, as they had never seen it before. Cap, gills, and hollow finely fibrillose stem all displayed the same colour (though paler at the stem base), the gills being almost free and wavy-edged. The reason for qualifying the name given above with "aff." is that true ***H. chlorophana*** is always described as having a greasy cap (even in dry weather), which our specimens did not have. So, this may be another species, unrecorded in the European books, and hence best not eaten even though ***H. chlorophana*** has been quoted as "edible".

26a *Hygrocybe aff. chlorophana*

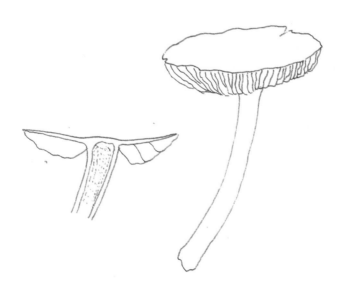

Equally attractive in colour is

26b Hygrocybe conica, with a sharply conical cap, that starts yellowish; often turning scarlet only to end black. The stem and flesh likewise change from yellow to black with age or injury. Gills almost free and scalloped. Notoriously variable, but perhaps more than one species involved in this country. So best not eaten, despite the EDIBLE assurance given in some books. Our young specimens were found near Alevkaya Feb. 1997, the older ones in a "fairy ring" in the lawn at the AN Graphics office in Lefkoşa, Jan. 2001.

26b Hygrocybe conica

Finally we have a rather common, all-white waxcap found on grassy banks under trees and variously assigned to the previous genus (as *H. nivea*), or to *Camarophyllus*, or nowadays named

27 *Cuphophyllus virgineus* (since identical with an American fungus first described from Virginia). Cap, flesh, gills and stem all white. Described as edible, but best left alone to avoid confusion with poisonous members of the genus *Clitocybe* (which however do not have the widely-spaced gills of the Waxcap family).

Found for example in shady places under pines near Esentepe.

27 Cuphophyllus virgineus

We now embark on the largest family in the book, all with white or near-white spores and non-crumbly flesh, but differing from the preceding **HYGROPHORACEAE** in not having thick wax-like gills, and from the following **AMANITACEAE** in that their gills are decurrent or sinuate and not easily separable from the stem.

We start with the genus *Lyophyllum,* characterised by growing in true clusters, i.e. several stems arising at the same point. A large species noted here is

28a Lyophyllum decastes (Gk "commander of ten men" because of growth in groups), with a fleshy, slightly convex, streaky, greyish-brown cap up to 10cm across, paler stem and slightly decurrent, fairly crowded, off-white gills of which many do not reach the centre. No marked taste or smell, but a good EDIBLE species if picked before insects attack it (this sp could be confused with *Entoloma lividum* which is not edible, but this has pink spores).
Seen here only in garigue beside the Buffavento dirt road, Jan. 2001.

28a Lyophyllum decastes

gills fairly crowded
with many not reaching
the centre

A much smaller fungus (cap to 2.5 cm across) with convex grey cap, rather close milky-grey gills and extremely tough though with hollow stem (grey shading to white above) appears to belong here. It had a distinctive grey spore print.

28b Lyophyllum sp*. This appeared, in single or paired specimens, on the Cengizköy golf course in Dec. 2001.

28b Lyophyllum sp.

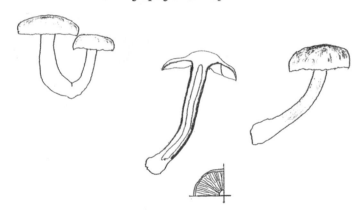

The genus *Clitocybe*, well represented in North Cyprus embraces most of our white-spored, smooth pale-capped fungi with a generally funnel-like clitocyboid outline and pale decurrent gills. Scent and taste should be noted while fresh, as these are often characteristic of a species. Most are highly poisonous, so let "taste and spit out" be the rule.

29a Clitocybe costata (Lat. "ribbed") is one of the commonest and most conspicuous species, with a smooth, deeply funnelled cap, ribbed at the edge and wavy when mature, russet-orange at first but becoming dirty white from the margin inwards. Stem cap- coloured. Smells of bitter almonds. Under pines, especially in the Alevkaya-Yayla area, Dec. 2000.

29a Clitocybe costata

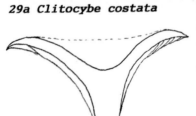

29b Clitocybe alexandri is perhaps the largest of the genus in this country (growing up to 15cm across the cap). Cap dull brown, smooth, flat at first but then depressed (sometimes more deeply than shown here). Gills pale, decurrent, stem of same colour, stout and thickening below. Found under coniferous or broadleaved trees abroad: here, isolated specimens recorded only in pinewoods above Essentepe. Dec. 1998

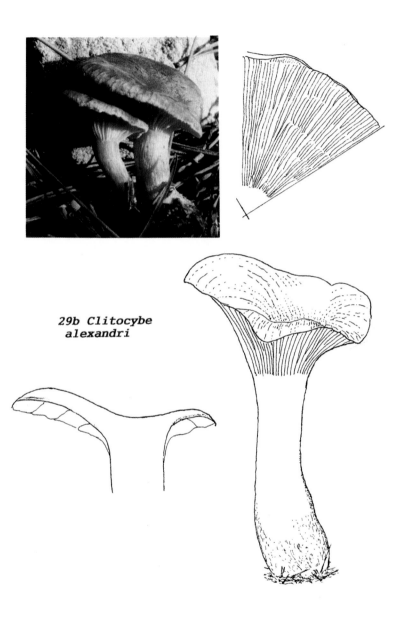

29b *Clitocybe*
alexandri

97

29c Clitocybe obsoleta (Lat. "common") has a white or buff-mottled cap, ivory white gills and often eccentric white stem. Smells strongly of aniseed (or Turkish drink Raki, Gk Ouzo). Sometimes found growing in "fairy rings" in moss under *Cistus* bushes, e.g. above Alsancak. Dec. 2001.

29d Clitocybe ditopus (Gk "double foot" from two stems often growing together) has a greyish-yellow dimpled cap, first convex but later flattish, gills and stem of the same colour and a strong mealy smell. It grows in a little cluster under pines, as on path side W. from Alevkaya, Nov. 2000.

29c Clitocybe obsoleta

29d Clitocybe ditopus

29e Clitocybe diatreta (Lat. from Gk diatrephō "to support" because of its growth on pine litter) is another small species found clustered in pine litter. The smooth, dimpled cap is russet brown aging paler, the gills and spore print pinkish (unusually for this genus) and slender stem likewise. Smell slightly fruity. Found under pines N. of Esenteppe, Nov. 2000

29f Clitocybe candicans (Lat. "white") has a pure white cap (only slightly depressed), gills (scarcely decurrent) and stem. No distinct smell. This group was found in central Girne, Feb. 2000

↑
single white
rhizoid growing
from stem base

29i Clitocybe vermicularis

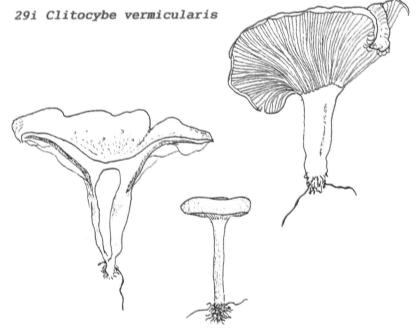

29j *Clitocybe augeana* (Lat. From the legendary "Augean stables" because of its growing on manure); also treated as a variety of the notoriously Poisonous ***Clitocybe dealbata.*** A luxuriant, almost deformed looking fungus with white cap, tan-tinted toward the centre, gills cream to light tan, similar coloured, often compressed or shapeless, hollow. In clumps on enriched soil, e.g. on sheep midden at Yeniceköy, Jan. 1998 and Bellapais, Jan. 1999

31 Omphalina sp

The genus *Tricholoma* itself is a vast one, most members having the typical convex, fleshy cap. Most are also white-spored, but we start with an exceptional light-yellow spored species,

32a Tricholoma fracticum (or *T. batschii*). Huge numbers appear around the New Year in e.g. the woods under Mt Yayla, pushing up the pine litter with their pinky-russet caps (up to 12cm across) and often being needlessly destroyed by fungus gatherers in search of tastier kinds. (It is not poisonous, but too bitter to enjoy.) It can be safely recognised by the rubbery stem, whose tan colour below the ring zone is sharply separated from the pure white above it. The gills are pale cream, darkening with age.

32a Tricholoma fracticum

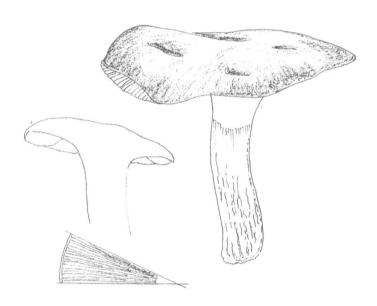

Our next two representatives of the genus *Tricholoma* are both white-spored.

32b Tricholoma terreum (Lat. "earth-coloured") occurs frequently in our pinewoods in mid-winter, often in large groups. Its flat-convex cap (to 8cm across) is either uniformly grey-speckled or has concentric zones of speckles. Gills and flesh are whitish-grey, the stem white, cylindrical, silky. Taste pleasant; EDIBLE.

32c T. portentosum (Lat. "marvellous", i.e. to eat). In its Cypriot form, this is an almost black-capped fungus (grey at first) with ochre gills. The brittle white stem which turns yellowish as it ages, is up to 10cm tall, hollow and swollen round the middle, pinkish just below the cap and often deeply buried in pine litter. Taste and smell mealy, but EDIBLE. Found here above Kozan, Jan. 2001.

32b Tricholoma terreum

32c Tricholoma portentosum

One of the most attractive late winter fungi in our pinewoods, and an excellent EDIBLE one, is familiar in England as the "Wood Blewit" and marketed in Europe, though overlooked (or foolishly destroyed) here. The light spores must always be checked as other lilac fungi, not yet found in Cyprus, with rusty brown spores (members of the Cortinariaceae) are highly poisonous

33 Lepista nuda (Lat. "naked", i.e. without the scales which the genus name implies). The cap and stem are often lilac or violet blue but vary with age and may dry out to a buff brown.. The rounded, in rolled cap-shape, rather close, wavy gills (blue, pink or white), and fibrous stem enlarged below, are further guides to identity as are the off-white spores. Quite frequent around Girne and Alevkaya in Jan.-Feb.

33 Lepista nuda

The genus *Myxomphalia* (Gk "slimy" though in this case merely smooth, + "navel" from the depressed cap-centre) has this one distinct species:

34 Myxomphalia maura (Lat. "moorish", from the dark cap), with its unmistakable helmet-shaped cap, deeply depressed in the middle, ranging in colour from greyish-black to tan, drying even paler, easily peeled. Gills whitish, spore print white. Stem smooth and tough. Taste sweetish. Often in troops on burnt ground, as in garigue N. of Buffavento dirt road, Jan. 2001.

34 Myxomphalia maura

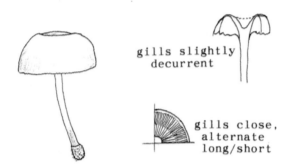

gills slightly
decurrent

gills close,
alternate
long/short

The genus *Collybia* (Gk "like a small coin") gives its name to one of the characteristic shapes of cap-and-gill fungi (see Key above, p.), viz. the "collybioid" outline – smaller, flatter and thinner-fleshed than the "tricholomatoid". The cap margin is more or less incurved, not flat as in *Mycena*. Unlike those of *Marasmius,* the stems of *Collybia* species split when twisted. One of the commonest here is:

35a Collybia dryophila (Gk "fond of oaks", its usual associate in Europe) that has a smooth, flat-convex, blotchy cream-to-orange cap (to 5cm across), stem in the same tones but white gills. In moss or grass under trees, from Oct. on.

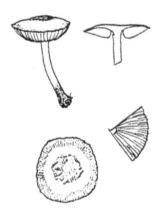

35a Collybia dryophila

Akin to *Collybia* is another large genus, *Marasmius* (Gk "shrivelling", i.e. not rotting when ripe). This genus also has smallish, thin-fleshed caps, and white spores. An unusual feature is that the dried fruit-bodies recover their shape when moistened. The stem is elastic, not splitting when twisted. All grow in vegetable debris.

36a Marasmius rotula (Lat. "little wheel") has its wide-spaced gills attached, not to the stem, but to a separate little collar. Cap whitish, diam. to 1.5cm; gills cream; stem black except for pale apex. In turf by Armenian Monastery, Nov. 2000.

36b Marasmius anomalus. Cap (to 1cm diam.) whitish, almost free from stem with no collar; gills whitish, wide-spaced; stem cream at apex, reddish to black below. In turf at Gönyeli, Jan. 1998.

36c Marasmius wynnei has a larger (to 5cm diam.), greyish cap; gills off-white; stem off-white above, brown-violet to black in lower half. Under pines below Alevkaya, Dec. 1998.

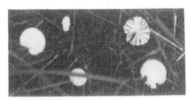

36a Marasmius rotula

underside
of cap 2X

underside
of cap 3X

36b Marasmius anomalus

36c Marasmius wynnei

123

Order **AGARICALES**   Family **TRICHOLOMATACEAE**

The genus *Crinipellis* (Lat."hair + skin") differs from its neighbours in having fine dark hairs pressed on to the cap, and hairy stem.

37 Crinipellis scabella (or *C. stipitaria*) has rings of russet hairs showing on a pale cap to 1.5cm across, off-white gills and a dark, stiff stem to 1.5cm diam. On dead grass stems, as at Gönyeli, Nov. 1997.

Members of the genus *Micromphale* (Gk "small + navel") resemble *Collybia* but have a narrow stem and are usually evil smelling.

38 Micromphale brassicolens (Lat. "cabbage-smelling") is immediately recognised by its rotten odour. Cap reddish-brown, aging darker and wavy; gills at first white, going brown from inner edge; stem reddish above, black and tapered below. In pine-litter, woods around Alevkaya. Nov. 2000

39d Mycena sanguinolenta

39e Mycena seynesii

39f Mycena pura (Lat. "clean, unmarked" from the uniform gills). Cap large for this genus (to 4cm), variable from pink to lilac with slightly denser centre; gills pinkish with no dark edge; stem-colour as for cap but pinkish below at base and thicker than most species (4-8 mm); smells of radish. In woods, e.g. pine woods above Kozan. Dec. 1998. Said to be POISONOUS.

39f Mycena pura

Order **AGARICALES**   Family **TRICHOLOMATACEAE**

The genus *Xeromphalina* (Gk "dry + navel") is marked by a leathery stem, and partial revival when moistened after drying, like *Marasmius*. Our species,

40 Xeromphalina fellea (Lat. "like gall"), is the only one described as bitter-tasting. It has an orange-yellow cap to 2cm across, gills passing from yellow to rusty and a slender stem, pale at the top, brown and then black below, with stiff "roots" at the bottom. Found under conifers, e.g. nr. Alevkaya, Jan. 1999.

The genus *Melanoleuca* (Gk "black + white", from the frequent combination of a dark cap and pale gills), is a very trying one for the amateur, as the many species here can only be differentiated microscopically, and do not always match any of those described in the available, i.e. European, textbooks. Broadly, speaking, putative *Melanoleucas* are fairly large with a flattish cap with raised centre (umbonate), cap-colour variable, gills pale and not decurrent. A common pale-capped example is the one shown here, tentatively dubbed "close to" *M. excissa* or, in academic style,

41 Melanoleuca aff. *excissa*. Cap cream with a raised tan centre, gills off-white, stem do. With supple spongy flesh, pale brown below. On bare soil, at Alevkaya picnic site, Feb. 2000.

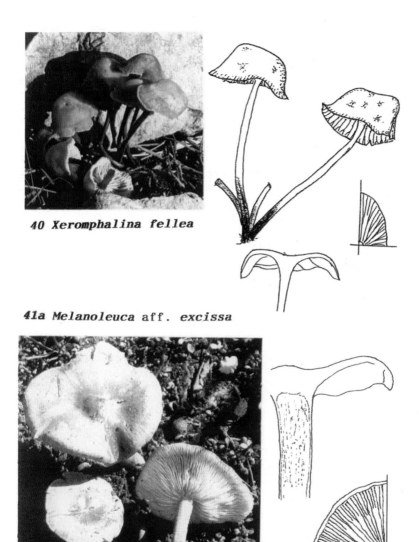

40 Xeromphalina fellea

41a Melanoleuca aff. **excissa**

41b Melanoleuca paedida In contrast, a small grey member of this difficult genus, superficially resembling the unidentified **28b Lyophyllum** sp. above. Cap grey, smooth slightly incurved with brown gelatinous flesh; gills white emarginated with slightly wavy edges. Stem smooth, tough, and ochraceous above; shading to dark grey in lower half. Under the microscope, the shallowly ornamented spores and "harpoon-like" cystidia confirm this name. Several isolated specimens found in moss under *Cistus* bushes above Arapköy, Feb. 2001

41c Melanoleuca brevipes A larger member of the group at 7cms across the grey cap; this again has the slightly incurved margin of the previous species. The gills are white, but dirty looking the stem is tough, rather lumpy and similar to the cap colour; it is short in relation to the cap width. Many specimens found on floor of gravel quarry on the ridge road. Further, specimens looking quite dissimilar, yellower in colour and with a much streakier cap proved to be the same species when viewed under the microscope it can only be assumed that some specimens were younger or had been growing in more favourable situations within the quarry. Both types are illustrated here.

41d Melanoleuca excissa A tentative confirmation of a collection of this species at the Alevkaya picnic spot from Feb 2000 introduces this section. However, a further collection is now confirmed from the turf at the Cengizköy golf course; with a 4cm wide leathery matt cap of light grey and a darker grey centre and with the characteristic in-rolled margin. Gills are white with a superficial flesh colour appearing when the fruitbody is tilted. The stem height is of similar dimensions to the cap diameter and the width is approx 5mm; the stem is a light flesh white colour. As with many species of Melanoleuca the entire fruitbody tends to grey or darken as it ages or dries.
At least a dozen specimens were growing together in short turf amongst clover on the sandy soil at Cengizköy golf course Dec. 2004

41e Melanoleuca rasilis var. rasilis A dark brown cap characterizes the specimen shown here with a beige brown stem approx. the same size as the diameter of the cap. The gills initially white with the margin that is concolorous with the cap but turning grey with age. The habitat in dunes is characteristic of these species, which can be found commonly throughout Europe. This specimen was growing alongside a broken log in the dunes to the east of Girne. Dec. 2004

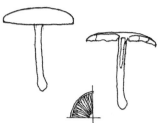

41b Melanoleuca paedida

41c Melanoleuca brevipes

41d Melanoleuca excissa   *41e Melanoleuca rasilis var rasilis*

135

The genus *Rugosomyces* (Lat. Gk "wrinkled fungus") was only recently separated on microscopic grounds from **Calocybe,** and that in turn from *Lyophyllum,* so all three names may be found applied to the two handsome species shown here.

42a Rugosomyces chrysenteron (Gk "gold gills") has indeed golden yellow gills, pale yellow stem and cap (to 6cm) gold or, centrally, brick-colour. Smell mealy and taste bitter. Mainly under *Spruce* in Europe, under pine (*Pinus*) here.

42b Rugosomyces onychinus (Gk "like onyx") has a reddish-brown cap, blackening with age, in rolled at the edge; the gills are pinkish-yellow aging to olive-yellow, stem lilac-pink. Both these species were found in pinewoods W. of Alevkaya, Dec.1998.

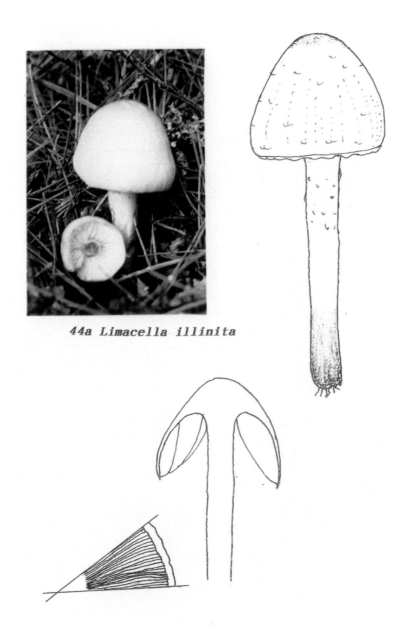

44a Limacella illinita

44b Limacella subfurnacea is a larger, flatter species with greenish-white cap and gills very distant from the stems, which is white above and fawn below. Occasional in pinewoods near Alevkaya and Akdeniz, Dec. 1998, 2000.

44b Limacella subfurnacea

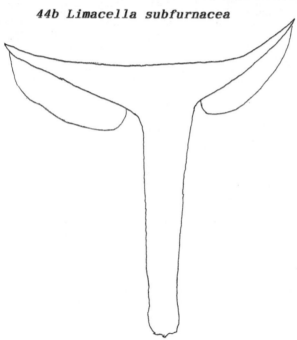

143

In the genus *Amanita* itself (Gk probably from Mt. Amanus now in Turkey) we find a surprising mixture of edible and poisonous, dull and handsome species. Their common feature in addition to white spores and free gills, is a bag (**volva**) round the base of the stem, making it important for identification to take the entire fruitbody. Many of the genus also have a ring, or at least a marked ring-zone part way up the stem, relic of the "partial veil" which initially linked the stem with the cap-margin, as well as fleecy patches on the cap remaining from the "universal veil".

45a *Amanita ovoidea* (lat. Gk. "ovoid" in shape when emerging) is a species tempting to eat and pronounced EDIBLE by some and POISONOUS by others; but compare its Cypriot look-alike 45b overleaf and the fatally poisonous "Deathcap" below 45d, before considering eating. (Many experts would advise against eating any Amanita sp.)

This is a giant among North Cyprus mushrooms, white all over but the cap (up to 25cm across) ages ochre in the centre and has fleecy patches both on the top and hanging from its margin. The stout stem is smooth above, shaggy below; the ring, which at first separates the two stem zones, soon falls off. The base is half hidden underground by the fawn volva, the young fruitbody looking like a white egg as it first breaks through it.

Occasionally under or near pines. The group shown, c. 15cm tall, stood beside an irrigation canal near Kalkanli, Nov. 1999. Rare in Europe this is definitely a "southern " species.

veil remnants

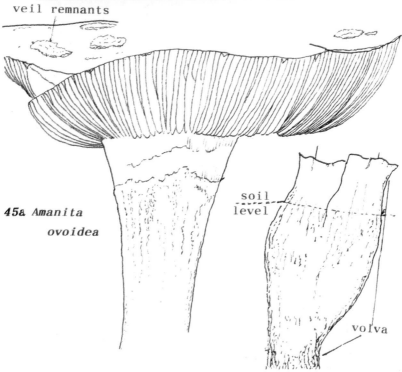

45a *Amanita*
    ovoidea

soil
level

volva

145

45b Amanita proxima resembles **A. ovoidea** except in having a russet volva. (pale cream /ochreous in **A. ovoidea**). They often grow together. This one, c. 20cm tall, was found on a gravely roadside nr Alevkaya, Nov. 1997. The species is described as POISONOUS.

45c Amanita aff. **malleata** (Lat. "with locks of hair", i.e. veil-patches). This name has been assigned to a species found here but once, near Alevkaya under a *Holly-leaved Oak,* Nov. 2000. Cap olive-grey with thick white veil-patches, the edge strongly striate. Stem olive, peeling to reveal white flesh. Loose volva.

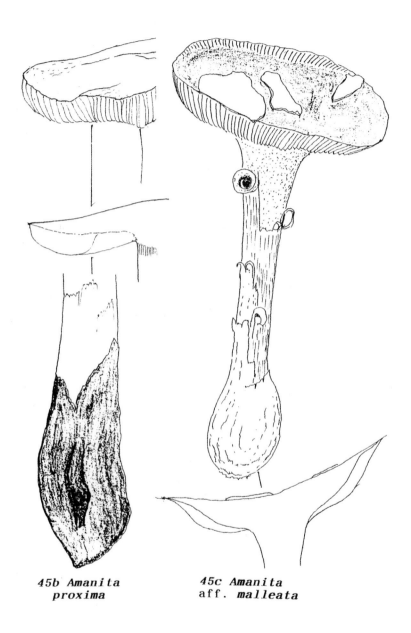

45b *Amanita*
proxima

45c *Amanita*
aff. *malleata*

45d The notorious "Death Cap", ***Amanita phalloides*** is shown here for comparison it is the fungus considered responsible for some 90% of "mushroom" fatalities worldwide, from kidney/liver failure after a deceptive remission of initial symptoms. Common in Europe especially under Beech and Oaks, it had not been seen by Nattrass but was included in his 1937 checklist of Cyprus fungi on the strength of reported symptoms of fungus poisoning. Nattrass gave no locations; the species was more likely to have occurred in what is now southern (Greek) Cyprus.

45e for completeness, we also show the picturesque and poisonous, but not lethally dangerous, "Fly Agaric", ***Amanita muscaria,*** once used as a fly-poison and, in some parts of the world, as a risky hallucinogenic. Nattrass also included this in his list for similar reasons, again without having seen it. It grows in Europe on acid soils; usually in association with *Birch* (*Betula sp.*) so is unlikely to turn up in the TRNC.

47 Pluteus aff. *cinereofuscus*

This entirely pink-spored family is difficult to explore without a microscope, since its only unifying element is not just the colour, but also the **shape** of the spores when magnified by 400X or more. (In the main genus, *Entoloma,* they are "prismatic" with several ± parallel faces; in *Rhodocybe,* they are small with many facets; in *Clitopilus,* they have lengthwise ridges.) We start with a few distinctive species of the first genus.

48a Entoloma aff. *hirtipes* (Lat. "hairy-foot".) This common spring species in pinewoods at Alevkaya and elsewhere has a reddish-brown umbonate cap (to 7cm) which dries paler; pinkish-yellow gills, and a long (to 12cm), slender, fibrous stem, brown except for the hairy white swollen base. It has a characteristic smell of cod-liver oil.

48b The shorter *Entoloma* aff. *undatum* (Lat. "wavy") has a creamy-grey cap (to 4 cm diam.) with concentric darker zones, often wavy-edged; gills and stem greyish; spore print pale rusty. Found on mossy ground under pines, e.g. nr. St Hilarion, Dec. 1998.

48a *Emtoloma aff. hirtipes*

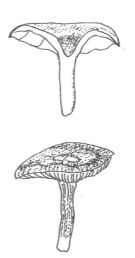

48b *Emtoloma aff. undatum*

48c Entoloma jubatum resembles *E. hirtipes* above, but has a velvety, smoky-grey cap and strongly fibrous, often spirally twisted stem. Gills ochre to chocolate but sporeprint salmon, flesh grey. Pinewoods e.g. near Alevkaya. Frequent Jan. 1998.

48d Entoloma phaeocyathus (GK "dusky goblet") belongs, like *E. undatum* above, to those of the genus which have a "clitocyboid outline" with strongly decurrent gills and a depressed cap. The cap in this species, however, is not zoned but blackish with a golden flush around the hollow, the gills dull red, the slender stem first dirty white, later charcoal-coloured. On the Cengizköy golf-course, Dec. 2001

.

48c *Entoloma jubatum*

48d *Entoloma phaeocyathus*

 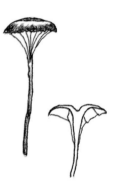

159

Two more pink spored, decurrent-gilled genera are exemplified here; *Clitopilus* (Gk "depressed head") and *Rhodocybe* (Gk "pink head").

48p Clitopilus prunulus "The Miller" This all-white fungus with a smooth wavy, centrally depressed cap, gills white turning pink, and downy stem has a mealy smell that has earned it the English name "Miller". Found in grass near trees, e.g. by the Eucalyptus grove below the Kanlıköy dam. Dec. 1998. Edible, and recommended, but rare here.

48r Rhodocybe popinalis (Lat. "pertaining to taverns", presumably suggested by the smell) is unmistakeable with its blotchy grey cap, grey gills, white to grey brown stem and thick whitish flesh. It tastes bitter and smells mealy; INEDIBLE. Grows in turf among pines, e.g. near the Ermeni evi below Alevkaya, Jan. 2001.

48p Clitopilus prunulus

48r Rhodocybe popinalis

48s Rhodocybe gemina (=truncate) shares the stout stem, in rolled cap-margin and decurrent gills of the previous species but its colours are in great contrast. The cap, often to 10 cm across, varies from leather tinted to cream but in this country is normally orange-yellow, smooth, dome-shaped but finally wavy; gills yellowish but spore print pink; stem white aging to cap colour. Smell and taste mealy. INEDIBLE. In pinewoods beside Gecitköy lake and E. of Akdeniz. Dec. 2001

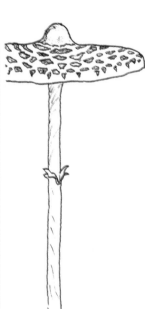

51 Macrolepiota konradii

Here follow two similar all-white agarics formerly grouped with others as *Leucoagaricus, meaning* just that. The first is now assigned to the well-named genus *Sericeomyces* (Gk "silky fungus"), as:

52 Sericeomyces serenus (Lat. "smooth"). The fresh cap is buff-coloured towards the centre, gills also buff but spore print pure white. The hanging ring is soon shed. The stem-base is markedly bulbous, but without a volva. Taste mild, edibility unclear, so best avoided. Under pines near Cengizköy, Nov. 1998.

54 Chamaemyces fracidus

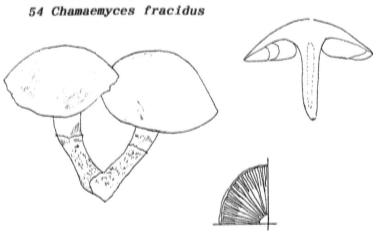

Finally, we come to the genus *Agaricus* comprising "mushrooms" in the narrowest sense, with light–capped but (when mature) dark gilled, stoutish stems with a ring (unless fallen) but no basal volva. Easily peeled and eminently EDIBLE fruit bodies. (Only one common species in Europe is "mildly" Poisonous, and is recognizable by the discolouration of the stem-base when cut, earning it the name "Yellow-stainer"; this has not been recorded here. Most of the other species when cut show a pink or brown stain, or none.)

The widely cultivated species *Agaricus bisporous* (i.e. with "two spores" on each fertile cell instead of the usual four, visible only with a microscope) grows wild on rich soil in Europe but has not been identified here. The nearest to it is the common

55a *Agaricus campestris* (Lat. "in fields", where indeed it grows. But the name "Field Mushroom" is applied to other species too). It has a pale, smooth, felty cap, convex and then flattening, with gills at first pink, then dark brown to black but giving a chocolate brown spore print. The stem carries a single ring at first, but this often disappears leaving only a "ring zone", above which the stem is smooth, while felty below. Usually in grassy fields or newly dug garden soil, e.g. Karaman, Feb. 1997

55b *Agaricus bitorquis* (Lat. "two circled") is another pale-capped, very stout-stemmed species in which the cap expands while still underground, then forcing its way up even through asphalt or against the weight of stone slabs. Gills pink, then dark brown. The stem carries two rings close together, which are persistent, the upper one the more prominent. Found in a stone quarry path. Beşparmak, Mar. 2000.

55a *Agaricus campestris*

55b Agaricus bitorquis

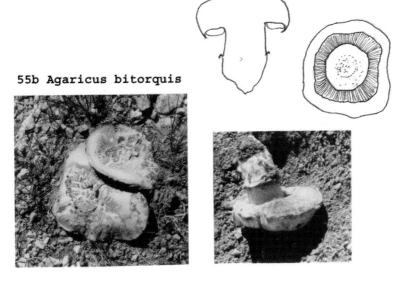

55c Agaricus porphyrrhizon (Gk " purple-rooted" has a cap covered with small chestnut reddish coloured scales except in the dark mahogany central disc; gills gelatinous beige, turning brown; stem white above, but fleecy and yellowish below the strong, drooping, ring; stem-flesh white, but yellow-spotted when cut and markedly yellow at the base, which sports conspicuous rhizoids (rootlets). Spore print light brown. Taste acrid; "NOT EDIBLE". Several groups found at the edge of a pinewood S. of Beşparmak. Dec. 2001.

55d Agaricus gennadii has a nearly smooth white cap and, in contrast to the other species shown here, no obvious ring but a sheath of dark-tipped scales up the lower part of the stem, which is cylindrical or tapered at the base. Smell strong; edibility unknown. Found under *Eucalyptus* trees at the Köprülü reservoir, Dec. 2000.

55c Agaricus
porphyrrhizon

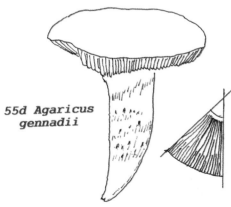

55d Agaricus
gennadii

55e Agaricus aff. **silvaticus** (Lat. "in woods") varies greatly in appearance and the cap of the specimen shown resembles rather that of two other species, **A. haemorroidarius** and **A. langei**. However, the former has a bulbous stem and the latter larger spores. All three, when cut, show a red stain (and are all EDIBLE) the one shown had an ochre cap with broad russet scales; pink gills, later brown; a tough, flexible stem with a strongly flaring, descending, ring, the stem being fleecy above the ring but smoothly fibrous below.

55e Agaricus silvaticus

55f Agaricus aff. **macrocarpus** (Lat. "large fruit-bodied)" is one of the biggest of the genus, with a smooth white or yellow-tinted convex cap, yellow when scratched and up to 15cm across, close-set gills darkening from pale pink to deep brown and a stout white stem, enlarging below and carrying a flaring ring in the upper half. As a yellow-staining species, it is probably slightly POISONOUS. In turf and pine litter, as in numbers at the Yayla turn-off Jan. 2001.

The only reason for qualifying the name with "aff." Is that the original description of the species speaks of coarse thick scales on the underside of the ring, which were not apparent in this collection.

55f Agaricus aff. macrocarpus

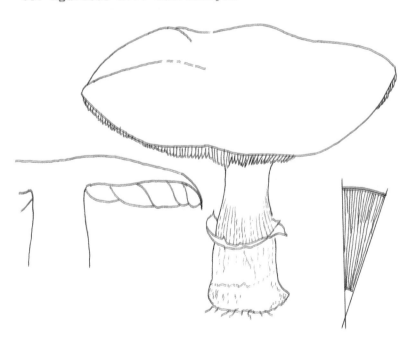

We end the treatment of this large family with two colourful members of the genus *Cystoderma* (Gk "scale-skin", referring to the stem sheath).

56a *Cystoderma amianthinum* (Gk "unspotted") has an ochre-yellow cap (to 8cm) becoming finely wrinkled; the stem is of the same colour with a mealy white sheath below the indistinct ring. Gills white, then yellow; spore print white. Chemical test: the cap turns red-brown with KOH. Frequent in pineland, e.g. nr. Alevkaya, Jan. 1998.

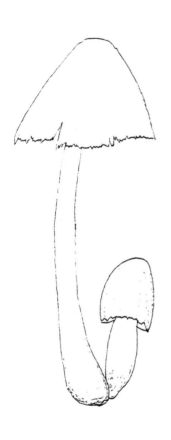

57c Coprinus domesticus

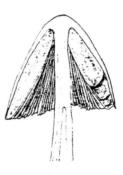

57d *Coprinus cinereus* (Lat. "ashen" the cap colour). Cap at first cylindrical, then bell-shaped, at first covered with a felty white veil which then breaks up to show a grey radially lined ground; gills white then blackening and deliquescing; stem white with a long rooting base. On manure, as here at Arapköy, Jan. 1999, in large numbers mixed with another, smaller, fungus on a sheep midden.

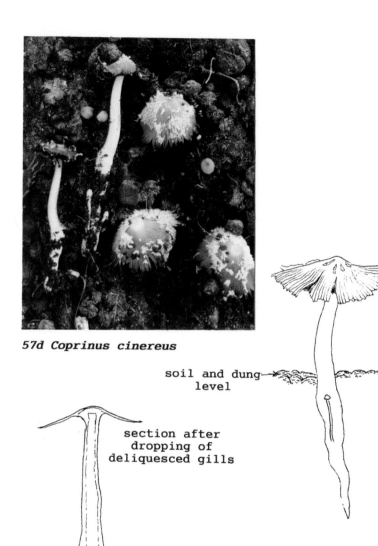

57d Coprinus cinereus

soil and dung
level

section after
dropping of
deliquesced gills

195

57e Coprinus plicatilis (Lat."with folds"), is one of the few members of the genus where the gills, though blackening, hardly deliquesce. The central disc of the cap, which starts conical but ends almost flat, is chestnut, the rest beige with grey "spokes" where the gills show through and give the whole fruitbody the look of a tiny Japanese umbrella. Gills quite free from the slender white, almost translucent stem. On turf and shady wood sides, as at the Ermeni evi near Alevkaya, Jan. 2001.

57f Coprinus cothurnatus (Lat. "booted") is, like C. cinereus above, a dunghill fungus. The fragile cap at first cylindrical, later expanded, carries a grey granular veil with light showing through between the gills. These are smoky grey with white edges, till they blacken and deliquesce. Stem soft and white, finely fleecy and bay coloured below. Stem base often enclosed, as shown, in a sheep dropping. Found on a midden-heap at Yeniceköy, Jan. 1998.

57g Coprinus aff. *flocculosus* (Lat."with little fleecy patches") has a white, at first conical, cap set with small erect fleecy white scales. Gills white, then blackening; stem white. In maturity, cap flat, radially split (as shown). Scattered individuals on side of tiny brook, Kalavaç, Apr. 2000.
Experts consulted hesitated in ascribing this collection to *C. flocculosus, C. bipellis* or the rare *C. xerophilus.*

57j Coprinus megaspermus

The genus *Panaeolus* (Gk. "variegated"), like the other two in this family, has black spores, but also the peculiarity that the spores do not ripen (and blacken) simultaneously over the whole gill and so produce a mottled appearance. The gills do not deliquesce as they do in *Coprinus* spp. In stature and cap shape, this genus is close to *Conocybe* in the next family, but those have brown spores, not black.

58a Panaeolus papilionaceus (Lat. "butterfly-like"). Cap dirty white with paler centre and slightly ridged margin; gills adnate, slightly mottled black with white edges; stem to 9cm high, dirty white; in wayside grass above Atifonitis Monastery. Dec. 2000.

58b Panaeolus aff. **olivaceus** (Lat. "olive-coloured." the gills). Cap greyish-fawn, hemispherical, slightly grooved round the edge, up to 2.5cm across; gills olive-brown; stem slender, fawn to 5cm. Found on burnt ground W. of Karaman. Dec.1999. Our collection almost matches the descriptions of this rare European species which has somewhat broader spores; hence the qualification "aff".

58a **Panaeolus papilionaceus**

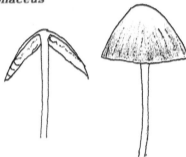

58b **Panaeolus** aff. **olivaceus**

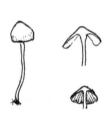

Another large genus in this family is **Psathyrella** (Gk. "crumbling") with fragile, usually slender stems, and gills dark but not mottled as in **Panaeolus**, nor deliquescent as in **Coprinus**.

59a Psathyrella bipellis (Lat."two-skinned" from 2-tone cap when drying) has cap to 3cm across, wrinkled and strikingly changeable. Olive-purple when wet, drying out patchily to pinkish-white; gills purple-to-black; stems slender, purple with paler base, aging pink. Found on buried or fallen wood, e.g. in turf among *Dittrichia (Inula)* shrublets in damp valley nr. Kalkanlī, Dec. 1999.

59b Psathyrella spadiceogrisea (Lat."date-brown and grey") also reacts to humidity changes, when wet.The cap (at first conical, then flattening) is olive-brown with white radial streaks; when dry, it goes white from the inside outward except for an orange-brown centre.The gills start white-grey, aging to violet-brown with a white edge. Stem pale, stringy. On mixed tree-litter, nr. Ermeni evi E. of Alevkaya, Jan. 2001.

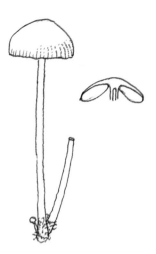

59d Psathyrella sp.

59e Psathyrella sp.

A very distinct member of the genus is:

59m Psathyrella lacrymabunda, commonly known as the "Weeping Widow" sometimes assigned to a distinct genus as **Lacrymaria velutina** (Lat. "weeping" + Lat. " velvety"). Usually tufted, the fruit-bodies have a felty, brownish-russet, later chocolate-brown, cap, first rounded later flat, weeping clear drops at the edge when young, gills snuff-brown then dark brown, the cortina and stem-ring stained black by the spores. Stem to 12cm tall, fibrous and darker below the ring. On soil and pine debris in a shaded courtyard, Karaman, Dec. 2000.
Described as "EDIBLE but bitter".

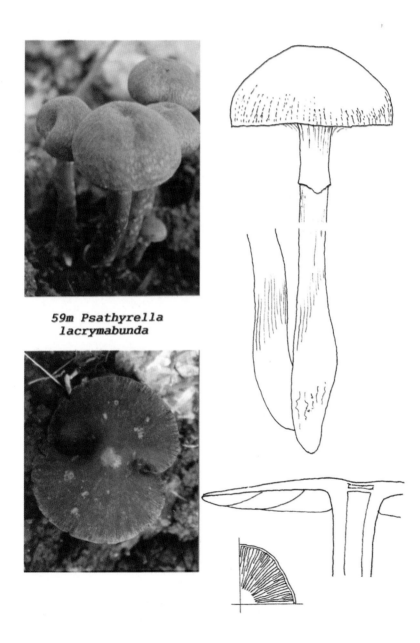

*59m Psathyrella
lacrymabunda*

211

A confusing, brown or black-spored family even for the expert, and evidently "polyphyletic", i.e. its various members are doubtfully related in the evolutionary tree and changes of name are accordingly frequent. Thus our

60 Bolbitius tener (lat. "cow-dung", on which some spp. thrive) (Lat. "fragile") has also been called *Conocybe lactea*. A truly fragile species with a slender cream-coloured cap, readily disintegrating, and pale, later rusty, gills. Stem pale, slender, sometimes with a small bulb. Found in manure-rich grass e.g. beside the Eucalyptus grove below the Kanlıköy dam, Dec. 1998.

61 Pholiotina filaris (diminutive of 63 *Pholiota*) (Lat. "thread-like") with its pale cap and stem, and rusty wide-spaced gills, looks like a tiny (0.5-1.5cm. diam.) *Galerina* but it has a distinct ring, first white then rusty, about 2/3 of the way up the stem. Also called *Pholiota filaris*, *Conocybe filaris* was found in moss on a sandstone valley floor near Kalkanlı, Feb. 2000.

63b Pholiota mixta

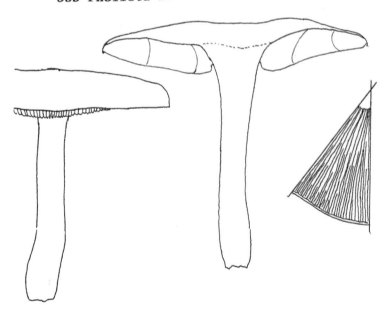

217

In this second genus, *Stropharia,* the spores are dark purplish and stain the sticky ring on the stem.

64a Stropharia aeruginosa (Lat. "verdigris-coloured") is unmistakable, not merely as the sole blue-green capped fungus to be found here, but also through the thick coat of slime forming on both cap and stem (and on the web-like "cortina" that at first connects them) from which white veil-scales can be seen projecting. Found hidden among *Carobs* above Lapta, Dec. 2000.

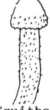

young fruitbody with
more veil on stem
than on cap

64a Stropharia aeruginosa

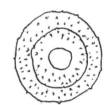

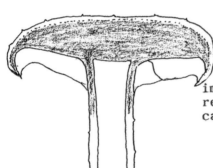

view from below;
immature cap with veil
remnants in slime on
cap and cortina, and
round stem

cap flesh mostly
gelatinous, with white
layer under skin

Order **AGARICALES**   Family **STROPHARIACEAE**

64b Stropharia coronilla is equally recognisable as the only fungus here with a pale yellow dry cap, combined with dark (grey-crimson) gills, plus a narrow ring stained with the falling spores; spore print dingy brown. Smells of radishes. Found in turf by Özhan reed-beds, Dec. 1998.

In the same family, we also find the genus *Psilocybe,* notoriously including the hallucinogenic "Liberty cap", *P. semilanceata.* The only species noted here, however, is

65 Psilocybe crobula with a small (to 1.5cm across), chocolate-brown, peelable fleecy cap (aging yellow), gills brown and slightly decurrent, stem brown with white, fleecy scales apart from a short bald ring-zone. On fallen pine-bark on the ridge-road W. from St Hilarion; Dec. 2000.

Ground
level

66a Gyrophragmium dunalii

225

Another huge family within another huge order, of which one can only say (microscopic details apart) that the gills are seldom free and the spores range from brown to black, never white or pink. *Cortinarius* itself boasts more species in Europe than any other, but is poorly represented here. And we start with a different genus, *Gymnopilus* (Gk "naked cap", not scaly) placed by some authors in the next family (**CREPIDOTACEAE**). This genus has only one, handsome, species reported here:

67 *Gymnopilus flavus* (Lat. "yellow"). Cap first foxy, then rusty-orange; convex but later flat, then depressed; gills yellow, then tawny like the spore print, sinuate then shortly decurrent. Stem solid, tawny with a white base. Tentative identification based on microscopic features esp. hyphae of cuticle. A large group found on soil with wood chippings nr. Cengizköy paper-mill, Dec. 2001.

67 Gymnopilus flavus

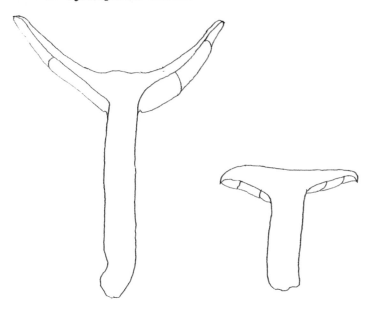

227

Within this great family, the genus best represented in North Cyprus is *68 Inocybe*, which translates from the Greek as "Fibre Caps". These are a somewhat undistinguished looking group of medium sized fungi with whitish to brown, convex to umbonate (raised-centre) caps, mostly patterned with fibres or scales and often cracked round the edge. The gills and spores vary from yellow to brown, and in many cases, the flesh is POISONOUS. In this country, they are largely found in turf or pine litter, living in mycorrhizal association with shrubs and trees. Identification of species is exceptionally difficult, depending a great deal on microscopic features such as the size shape and siting of sterile cells called cystidia. We show a few representative species; there are no doubt many more waiting to be determined.

68a Inocybe dulcamara (Lat. "bitter-sweet") is one of the more distinct species, having a scurfy cream-to-brown cap and yellowish-buff gills that age darker and give a tawny spore print. The stem is rather slender and usually crooked. In young specimens there is a distinct cortina (veil) connecting the cap margin with the upper stem. Smells somewhat of honey; tastes slightly bitter. A common spring species found in small troops in turf, under *Cistus* and at wood edges. In Karaman as late as May 2000.

68a Inocybe dulcamara

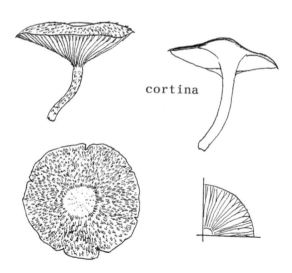

cortina

68b Inocybe aff. ***bongardii***. A species characterised by its fruity smell (usually likened to ripe pears) and narrow white fringes on the otherwise brown gills. The cream-to-tawny cap is covered with slightly darker, close-lying little scales and may age pink at the margin; there are similar scales on the upper part of the stem. In pine litter N. of Alevkaya. Feb. 1999 (name tentative: in Europe the species is associated with broadleaved trees.)

68c Inocybe pisciodora (Lat. "smelling of fish") is sometimes treated as a variety of the foregoing but has a contrasting fishy smell; gills beige, aging brown. Numerous in *Cistus* turf above Tazīk Viran, Feb. 2000.

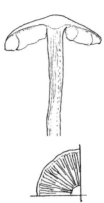

68b Inocybe aff. **bongardii**

68c Inocybe pisciodora

68d Inocybe flocculosa is a gregarious species with a markedly humped, pale tawny cap, with dark brown fibrils radiating over a fleecy skin. The gills start pale fawn, later cinnamon; the spindle-shaped, crystal-tipped sterile cells (cystidia) on their sides and edges are just visible with a x20 lens. Stems slender, first whitish, then beige. Under *Cistus* and *Inula* shrublets on a sandstone valley floor near Kalkanli, Feb. 2000.

A slight variant of the above is:

68d Inocybe flocculosa var crocifolia, with gills yellow not cinnamon, and a yellow stain on the upper part of the stem. Found E. of Alevkaya on ridge road near old "British camp", under pines Jan. 2002

68e Inocybe lacera (Lat. "ragged") has a snuff-brown, slightly humped cap with scurfy scales, pink to russet gills, stem ochre, aging darker and even reddish-black at the base; smell spermatic. On stony path in pine woods W. of Alevkaya. Feb. 1998.

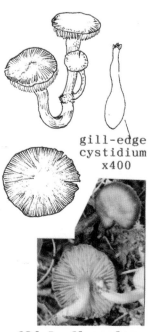

gill-edge
cystidium
x400

68d Inocybe flocculosa

68d I. *flocculosa*
var. *crocifolia*

68e Inocybe lacera

edge of cap
x10

68f Inocybe griseovelata (Lat. "grey-veiled") is a short-stemmed species with the stem enlarged upward: the brown cap is covered with a grey veil; the gills are pale brown with grey fibrils. Found on a stony path through pinewoods above Esentepe, Dec. 1999 (but in Germany under broadleaved trees).

68g Inocybe obscurobadia (Lat. "dark chestnut") has despite its name a pale brown cap covered with fine fibrils, and with small scales near the centre. Found under pines at Anthos near Çamlibel, Jan. 2000.

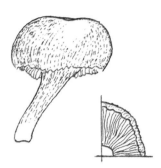

68f Inocybe griseovelata

68g Inocybe obscurobadia

68b Inocybe aff. *nitidiuscula* (also called *I. friesii*) has a cap with date-brown streaks radiating over a paler ground, suede brown gills and a lighter stem markedly thicker toward the base (or even bulbous, raising doubts to identity). Smell spermatic; found in moss under pines near ruined church E. of Alevkaya, Feb. 1997.

68i Inocybe aff *sindonia* is the only more-or-less all white species of the genus recorded here, with the cap slightly darker at the centre, the gills creamy and the stem swollen at the base. Found in pine-litter at the Yayla turn-off above Alevkaya. Jan. 2002.

68h Inocybe
  aff. *nitidiuscula*

 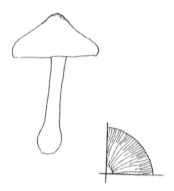

68i Inocybe aff. *sindonia*

The genus Cortinarius itself (named after the web-like "curtain", Lat. Cortina, or "partial veil" connecting the cap-margin with the ring-zone on the stem in young specimens) is one of the largest in Europe but poorly represented in Cyprus. The first to be identified was

69a Cortinarius dionysae with the thick stem, swollen below, typical of the genus. The cap is brownish ochre streaked with grey fibrils, the gills bluish grey, stem ring zone rusty brown from cortina and spore colour. The flesh smells mealy and reacts brown to alkalis. Found in the *Cistus* garigue (opp. Beşparmak mts.) succeeding burnt conifer and broadleaved stands, Dec. 2000.

69a Cortinarius dionysae

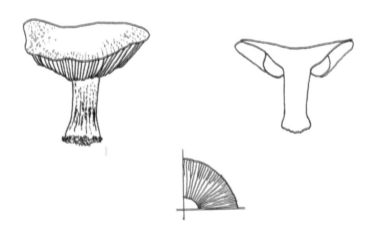

This second, unidentified

69b _Cortinarius_ sp*. With a fawn greasy cap, mustard-brown gills and spore print and thick whitish buff stem (not swollen below) was also found in _Cistus_ and _Lentisk_ garigue on burnt ground, just N. of the Buffavento track, Jan. 2001.

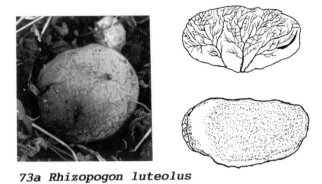

73a Rhizopogon luteolus

73b Rhizopogon vulgaris

Our first, puzzling genus *Omphalotus* (Gk "navel" + "ear") in this very heterogeneous family is sometimes relegated to a family **OMPHALOTACEAE** on its own, sometimes to the previous order **AGARICALES**. Here we have followed the Kew arrangement by grouping it with the next two genera as family **PAXILLACEAE**

74 Omphalotus olearius, with its large orange-gold cap and stem, orange flesh, golden and strongly decurrent gills (but white spore print) is perhaps the only Cypriot fungus to shine in the dark (apart, possibly, from the "Honey Fungus" *30 Armillaria mellea).* The luminescence is only apparent in complete darkness here, but in America has earned the fungus the name "Jack-O'-Lantern". A POISONOUS parasite, on *Olive* trees (whence the Latin specific name) in the Mediterranean region. In Britain, it is a rarity on other broadleaved trees.

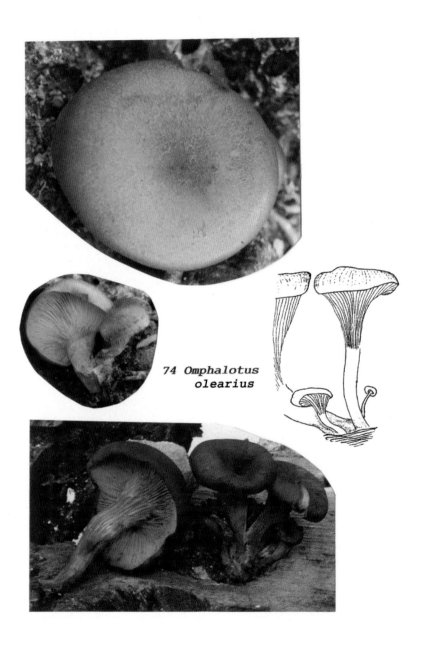

74 Omphalotus olearius

The genus Paxillus itself comprises a few stout-stemmed, firm-fleshed species, of which only one has been seen here:

75 *Paxillus panuoides*. The fruitbody is spoon shaped, dirty white above but yellow-orange below, with the cap margin strongly inrolled, the gills deeply decurrent down the lateral stem. Found either growing in tiers on dead conifer stumps (e.g. at Karaman 2000) or on ground debris probably attached to hidden roots (Cengizköy 1998). NOT EDIBLE (The dangerously POISONOUS "Rollrim", *Paxillus involutus*, so common in Britain has not been noted here.)

With its slender, central stem and whitish cap (and gills at first, but later buff) **76 *Ripartites tricholoma*** (GK "hair-edged") differs from the preceding members of the family, though like them it has a markedly inrolled cap margin. It unique feature is the row of short upright hairs visible round the edge of the cap when fresh. Occasional on soil under pines, e.g. Alevkaya, 1998.

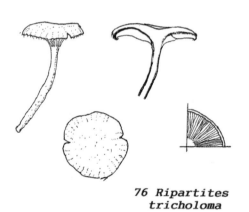

**76 Ripartites
tricholoma**

253

This family groups several genera of "Boletes" – fungi with pores rather than gills on the underside of the cap. Modern research, however suggests that they are not all closely related in evolutionary terms and we have seen one genus Polyporus, which has pores but is obviously very different from the stout-stemmed members of the genus Boletus, whose fruit-bodies (Fr. "Ceps", Ital. "Porcini", Ger. "Edelpilze") provide such an abundant harvest of delicacies in the autumn woods, esp. *Oak, Beech* and *Pine* of Europe. (A few are inedible, only one the "Satan Bolete" is seriously poisonous: it does not occur in Cyprus.) The only true bolete recorded here is

77 *Boletus rhodopurpureus*, with a russet, slightly sticky cap, which goes blue after a few seconds when bruised. The cap and stem flesh are white, turning blue when cut, but soon reverting to white. The pores are crimson, going blue when touched and remaining so. The yellow stem likewise bruises blue; it is covered with a red network breaking up below into lines of red dots. A single, aged specimen was found in a coniferous area E. of Esentepe, Nov. 1997, under an isolated pair of broadleaved trees (*Carob* and *Holly-leaved Oak*).

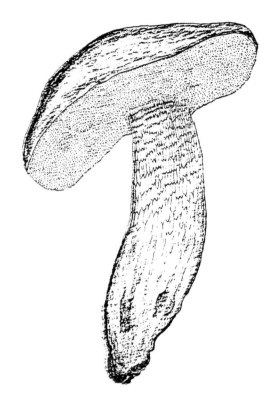

77 Boletus rhodopurpureus

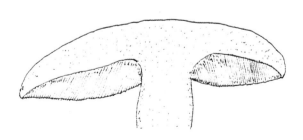

pores x10

Suillus (Lat."little pig". Cf Ital."Porcino", though this is applied to the edible Boletes in general). A genus akin to *Boletus*, but mostly with sticky caps and yellowish pores running shortly down the stem. A few have stem-rings but most do not.

78a Suillus bellini belongs to a group with dark granules (more conspicuous than in our photographs) on the upper part of the stem, but no ring. Fleshy creamy. The cap colour is variable, sometimes starting white and going yellow-to-russet, sometimes much darker except for a pale rim (lower photograph). Stem stout above, but tapered downward. In pinewoods (near Esentepe) under isolated broadleaved trees (*Carob* and *Oak*). Nov. 1999 below and again in Jan. 2000.

78a Suillus bellini

granules
on stem
x10

*78b **Suillus mediterraneensis*** has a persistently yellow cap and flesh; the stem likewise, with dark granules all over. Fairly common in most seasons in pine litter. These were found at the Yayla turn-off above Alevkaya, Jan. 2001.

*78c **Suillus granulatus*** is distinguished by its orange–russet cap, clear droplets forming on the spore-bearing surface in maturity, and by dark granules appearing only at the top of the stem. Less common than the foregoing, found in the same area Jan. 2002.

78b Suillus mediterraneensis

78c Suillus granulatus

We finally come to two more tube-bearing genera akin to boletus. One is *Xerocomus* (Gk "dry" + " hair" – the dry, velvety cap contrasting with *Suillus* spp. above).

79 *Xerocomus* aff.*chrysenteron* (Gk "golden within") is so-called because the maturing cap appears to crack into irregular dark patches, revealing a red or yellow ground-colour in between. Most striking is the immediate blueing of the yellow pores and upper part of yellow stem, if touched, and of the tubes, if cut. The blue fades after a few minutes, except for the tubes. A single specimen (hence the tentative naming) was found in the roadside pine litter above Esentepe, Nov. 2000.

A second colourful genus, ***Chalciporus*** (GK "copper-pored"), has a slightly sticky cap, far less so than *Suillus* spp. This is represented here by the rare

80 *Chalciporus amarellus* (Lat. "bitterish"), with a slightly scabby, ochre cap, white flesh, handsome crimson pores (round or, near the stem, longish) and a solid, pale yellow stem. The taste is mild, despite the Latin name. Under pines N. of Alevkaya. Jan. 1998

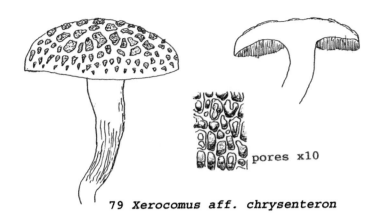

pores x10

79 *Xerocomus aff. chrysenteron*

80   *Chalciporus amarellus*

pores x3

Chroogomphus, (Gk " skin-colour" + "large headed nail") a small genus of decurrent- gilled fungi notably

*81 **Chroogomphus rutilus*** (Lat. "russet"), with a copper-coloured to vinaceous, sticky or shiny cap up to 8 or even 12 cm across, with well-spaced gills and cylindrical stem of the same colour but paler above the distinct ring-zone, mottled below. Flesh yellow-ochre near the cap-skin, darker below and orange at the stem base. Taste slightly bitter according to one textbook, "edible but not recommended". A handsome species; growing in short turf under pines, e.g. nr. Alevkaya, Jan. 1998.

81 Chroogomphus rutilus

An enormous order, comprising roughly, all the mushroom-like fungi; (i.e. with distinct stem, cap and gills) in which the texture of the flesh is crumbly rather than fibrous. A microscope shows that this is due to the presence of numerous round cells (as against long thread-like cells) in the flesh, which enable fragments to separate easily. The family has two main genera:

Lactarius in which cut or damaged specimens yield a white or coloured liquid; and **Russula** in which they do not. Several species are edible, many not. None have a ring round the stem; nor a volva (sac) around the base.

Fungus enthusiasts in Europe spend much of their time identifying the members of these enormous mycorhizal, tree-associated, genera and are disappointed to find how few occur in our dry, limestone-based, almost exclusively coniferous woods.

Genus **RUSSULA** (Lat. "reddish", as a few are). Identification of species depends on several factors – colour, taste, smell, ease of peeling, spore print colour etc. – which do not need a microscope, but DO require fresh material. Four tentatively identified species have been found here; three have reddish caps, slightly decurrent gills and a bitter taste, and are believed POISONOUS.

82a Russula luteotacta (Lat. "yellow when touched") has a pink-flushed cap, white stem (slowly yellowing when bruised) and white spore-print. In Europe, associated with broad-leaved woods, and found here (once, near Antiphonitis, Nov. 1997) under *Oak* and *Carob* isolated among pines.

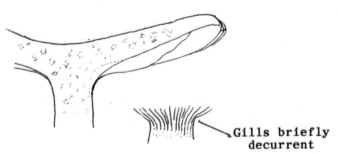

Gills briefly
decurrent

82a   Russula luteotacta

Order **RUSSULALES**   Family **RUSSULACEAE**

This second species
82b Russula sanguinea or **sanguinaria**, differs in having a bright red cap, often pink flushed stem and pale yellow spore print. Found here in Tazīk Kīran pinewood (Dec. 1998) and below Mt. Yayla.

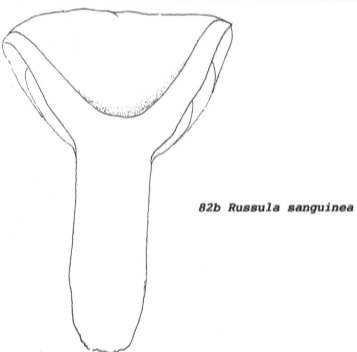

82b Russula sanguinea

267

82c Russula delica belongs to a subgenus (**Compactae**) of mostly pale species, which have numerous short gills amongst the long ones extending from cap-rim to stem. Cap blotchy, yellowish-white; gills and spore print white to cream. Stem white, thick and firm. Taste acrid. Common in Europe under broadleaved and coniferous trees; here found in pine-litter at the Yayla turn-off. Nov. 2000.

82c Russula delica

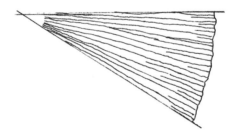

82d Russula torulosa differs from the above species in having a cap that is a rather more purple in hue and a stipe that can have ± deep pink colouration on it or be totally white.The spore print is pale yellow.This species is common on coastal dunes with *Pinus nigra* in Europe and in UK. Found under pine Dec. 2004

82d Russula torulosa

The other large genus in this family, *Lactarius* (Lat. lac, "milk"), is distinguished by the white or variously coloured liquid, which exudes from the gills or stem when injured. The gills are sloping to somewhat decurrent. The cap is usually depressed, even funnel-shaped. There are poisonous and edible species in both genera; to be sure of identifying any specimen correctly, it is important to note both taste and smell when fresh, and if possible to take a spore print (see preface) as soon as possible.

83a Lactarius deliciosus – the "Saffron Milkcap" or, for Turkish Cypriots, *Kırmīzī mantar* or *Dağ mantarī* – is the most reliably EDIBLE fungus, prized throughout Europe, and most commonly marketed in North Cyprus after *10 Pleurotus eryngii var ferulae*. It is however, far less common, enjoys only a brief season (Nov.-Jan.) and in some years hardly appears at all. The cap, sometimes as large as 12cm across, varies from yellow to brownish orange with darker zoned blotches, greening slightly (like the gills and stem) when bruised; gills orange, exuding carrot coloured drops when cut which do not change colour; stem paler with orange pits. Grows under pines or among *Terebinth* shrubs, e.g. between Alevkaya and the Beşparmak hills.

83a Lactarius deliciosus

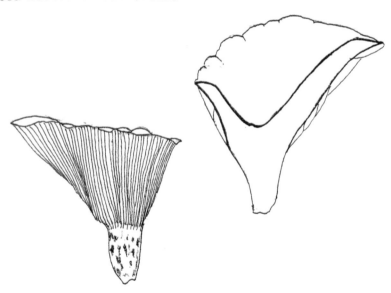

This and the following four orders bring us to the Cypriot representatives of the Gasteromycetes, fungi in which the spore-bearing cells or basidia, instead of being arranged on the surface of gills or pores (or spikes under the cap in some non-Cypriot genera) are placed INSIDE the variously-shaped, hollow fruit-bodies. The first order contains two families immediately recognisable from their English names, the "Earth-stars" and the "Puff-balls" respectively.

84a Geastrum triplex (Gk "earth star") like the rest of the genus, has an unmistakeable fruitbody consisting of a round spore-sac or endoperidium covered in a thick outer skin or exoperidium which splits into a number of "arms"; these curl back on to the ground, and so raise the spore–sac into the air; the spore mass or gleba, when mature, is then expelled through a central pore. In this species there are 5-8 arms, first creamy then russet brown, which in maturity crack up into squarish blocks, with the fawn spore–sac resting on a "dish", this third, fleshy layer is denoted by the name "triplex" – between it and the exoperidium. Found by path in pine wood N. of Alevkaya, Jan. 1999

84b Geastrum sessile (lat. "sitting" directly on the exoperidium also called *G. fimbriatum*) differs from the previous species in having no "dish" under the spore sac. The whole fruitbody is paler and smoother. Found each year, in numbers, esp. on one grassy bank under pines on the road between Yayla and Esentepe.

section through
spore-sac,
"dish"
exoperidium

exoperidium
from below

84a *Geastrum triplex*

84b *Geastrum sessile*

84c Geastrum berkeleyi is a smaller species in which the powdery grey spore-sac is supported by a narrow neck, and has its apical pore surrounded by 4-5 erect black "teeth" – a "peristome". Found here and there in pine litter under Mt. Yayla, Dec. 2001

84d Geastrum pseudolimbatum is a miniature, grey-legged species in which the white spore sac is only c.1cm in diam. Found on a bare patch of sandy soil at the Cengizköy golf course, Dec. 2001.

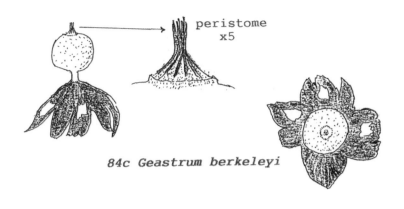

peristome
x5

84c Geastrum berkeleyi

84d Geastrum pseudolimbatum

The genus *LYCOPERDON* (Gk "wolf's fart", fancifully, from the cloud of spores emitted by the ripe "puff-balls") is represented in Cyprus by the common

85 *Lycoperdon perlatum* (Lat. "very widespread"), also called *L. gemmatum*, whose light brown club shaped fruitbody is at first covered with little conical spines; these soon fall off to leave a mesh pattern. The spore-mass inside is first white, then olive-brown and powdery, separated by an indistinct membrane from the sterile large–celled base. The spores are emitted through a jagged hole in the centre of the ripe "club" when knocked or struck by raindrops. Found in groups on soil under pines, e.g. around Alevkaya.

86 *Vascellum pratense* (Lat. "of meadows" – earlier called *Lycoperdon pratense*) has a similar structure, but is top-shaped, with a continuous internal membrane between the gleba and the sterile base, and a smooth un-patterned skin after the short warts fall off. Here too the spores escape through an irregular central pore. Found in turf, e.g. on the Cengizköy golf - course, Dec. 2001.

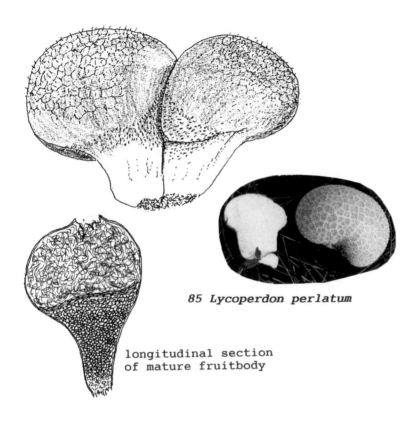

85 Lycoperdon perlatum

longitudinal section
of mature fruitbody

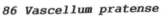

86 Vascellum pratense

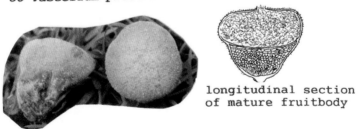

longitudinal section
of mature fruitbody

Order **LYCOPERDALES**   Family **LYCOPERDACEAE**

The genus **Bovista** can be found in Cyprus in dry grassy habitats, typically old dune slack systems. They can often be found blowing or rolling around on the ground as small puff balls, each bounce causing the papery dry exterior to puff out the spores through a small slit in the exterior casing. Represented here by two species:

87a Bovista plumbea the "Lead-Grey Bovist" looks very much like a small (2cm) smooth white golf ball when young, however as the fruitbody matures the outer fleshy coating peels away to reveal a lead coloured inner ball which contains the sepia coloured spores all mixed within a fine fibrous mass. Found in the turf at the Cengizköy golf course 2001.

87b Bovista nigrescens the "Brown Bovist" Initially superficially similar to the above species, however as the fruitbody matures the outer coating does not peel off as a separate coating; instead the thinner outer casing begins to split into flaky adhering particles which eventually disappear revealing a brown shiny inner ball. The interior contains the spores that are dark brown purplish; again mixed in the fibrous mass. Found in the turf at the Cengizköy golf course 2001.

87a *Bovista plumbea*

87b *Bovista nigrescens*

Genus *TULOSTOMA* (Gk "knob-mouth", i.e. round-head). A small group of puffballs with slender stalks and a basal sac, opening by a small pore in the centre of the head.

The species recorded here (in turf around the ruined church W. of Alevkaya, Jan.1999) appears to be

88 Tulostoma squamosum with scaly stem and no brown ring round the central pore (unlike the British rarity *T. brumale).*

Genus *BATTARRAEA*. Perhaps only two species world wide, with orange heads supported by uniquely persistent, woody stems, emerging in summer from an underground "egg". The British *B. phalloides* has only been seen once or twice; the Cyprus specimens belong to

89 Battarraea stevenii, differing in that the underground part is dry throughout, not gelatinous. It grows to some 5kg and is highly EDIBLE, never maggoty. Not till June do the stems rise up (one grown in an empty house reached 52cm!) and drop the white inner peridium and volva-remains, exposing the soft orange gleba, which continues to shed spores for months. (These are applied as natural anti-chafing talc to the necks of donkeys – a second reason for the Turkish vernacular name "Donkey Fungus".)

This species is abundant under olives in the village of Beyköy, near the old paper-mill at Cengizköy and sporadically elsewhere. It is recorded from warm climes worldwide.

section

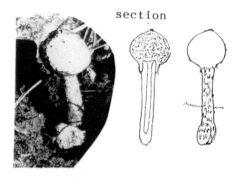

88 *Tulostoma squamosum*

troop in turf

89 *Battarraea stevenii*

two fruitbodies,
fallen peridium
and volva from
righthand cap

illustration
continued

283

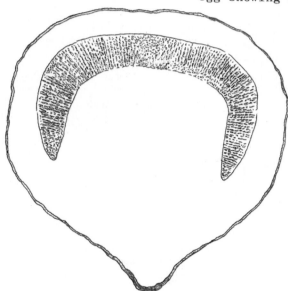

section through mature
egg showing orange gleba

89 Battarraea stevenii

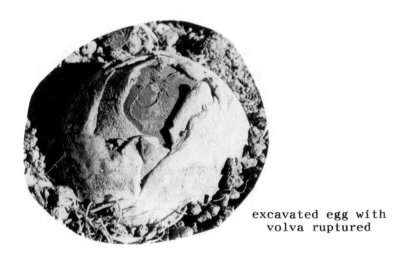

excavated egg with
volva ruptured

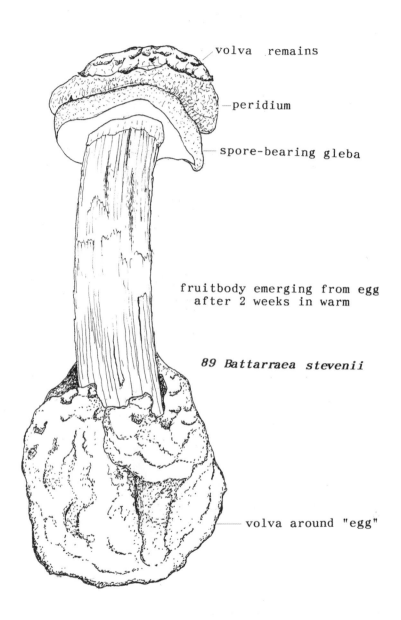

volva remains

peridium

spore-bearing gleba

fruitbody emerging from egg
after 2 weeks in warm

89 Battarraea stevenii

volva around "egg"

Order **NIDULARIALES**   Family **NIDULARIACEAE**

The strange group of small "bird's nest fungi" (as the Lat. name implies) growing on wood or plant remains, the fruitbody spherical at first, then splitting above to reveal several hard "eggs" (peridioles) in which the spores develop.

90 Cyathus olla (Gk for "cup" + Lat. for "pot") the mature fruitbody is like an inverted bell, shaggy outside; the peridioles are smooth, pale, lens-shaped, scattered by falling raindrops. Common in Europe, here found once at Kanlıköy, Dec. 1998, on a heap of plant remains.

Order **SCLERODERMATALES**   Family **SCLERODERMATACEAE**

Genus *Scleroderma* (Gk "rough-skinned"). Consists of rough, roundish "Earth-balls" with a distinct stalk and "roots", the cap opening irregularly to release the dark mass of spores.

The specimen shown of

91 Scleroderma verrucosum (Lat."warty") consists of several fruit-bodies fused together, growing on soil beside a concrete step (Karaman, Nov.1997). Normally the fungus grows under broadleaved trees and the cap is covered with small brown scales.

top and side views

90 Cyathus olla

91 Scleroderma verrucosum

side view

Order **SCLERODERMATALES**   Family **SCLERODERMATACEAE**

Genus *Pisolithus* (Gk "pea-stone" from the peridioles, see below) has apparently only one species, though variously named at different times. We restrict ourselves to one synonym.

92 Pisolithus arrhizus (Gk "without roots"), a large brown shapeless fungus (often two fused together) with a grooved column, extending underground, and flattened cap with a thin skin. The fertile, inner mass or gleba is pale at first, then dark brown as the spore-containing pea-size peridioles develop. On light soil, often in troops, the older specimens resembling dry powdery dung. Rated inedible – but no doubt seldom tried.

Possibly originating in Australia, where it is associated with Eucalyptus, and found here under Eucalyptus near Vadili, but elsewhere under other trees or none. Widely scattered here, very rare in the UK. Sporadic in warm parts of Europe.

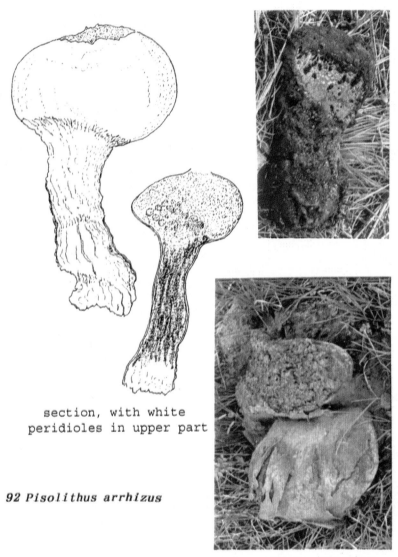

section, with white
peridioles in upper part

92 Pisolithus arrhizus

two old fruitbodies

289

Genus *PHALLUS* (Greek for the erect male member) is a small but unmistakable genus of saprophytic fungi (two species in UK) which start as a half-buried round "egg", surprisingly edible at this stage, with a jelly-like "gleba" – the inside layer containing the future spores. Our species is vividly named

93 Phallus impudicus (Lat. "shameless"). As the egg ripens over several weeks, the fruitbody breaks through the skin and extends as a white, honeycombed stalk to about 20cm high, its oval head covered with a dark slime whose carrion-like smell can be detected far and wide.This attracts flies, which pick the head clean before flying off, so dispersing the spores.

English "Stinkhorn". Common in Europe but only noted here once, in Karaman Jan. 2001, on bank under *Cistus.*

young "egg"

two erect fruitbodies

fly cleaning the gleba

head sipped clean

93 Phallus impudicus

291

Genus *COLUS*, containing the single species

94 Colus hirudinosus, whose fruitbody, arises from a small (1 cm. diam.) egg with cord-like "roots" on the surface of soil or pine-litter. The short stem divides into 4-6 separate pinkish columns supporting a cage-like network of corrugated arms, with an olive-coloured spore-bearing layer on the inside.

Found here twice, in grass at Bellapais and on a pinecone heap at Karaman, Feb.-March 2000/01. Also recorded from Jamaica, Palestine, Nigeria and warm parts of Europe.

Another southern European member of the family, *Clathrus ruber*, with a striking red, hollow cage is a rarity in the UK and was recorded from Cyprus (locality unspecified) in 1937.

fruitbody in grass

94 Colus hirudinosus

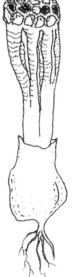

ruptured
"egg"

fruitbody in pine litter

HETEROBASIDIOMYCETES

The next two orders belong to the Heterobasidiomycetes, i.e. the second division of the Basidiomycetes; in these the spore-bearing cells or basidia are "septate", i.e. with transverse or longitudinal cross-walls – all visible only under a high-powered microscope.

Order **TREMELLALES**   Family **TREMELLACEAE**

Genus*TREMELLA* (Lat. "tremere", to shake). A fairly large genus of jelly-like fungi. Starting out as a smooth cushion growing on dead wood, becoming increasingly wrinkled, with the spore-bearing surface outside. The species shown,

95 *Tremella mesenterica* (Gk "intestine-like"), is well described by the English name "Yellow Brain Fungus". It is common in Europe on broad-leaved tree-stumps but was found here on the cut surface of a Pine, near Alevkaya, Dec. 2001.

Genus ***EXIDIA***. Another gelatinous group, of varied colour, again forming wrinkled patches on dead wood, but firmly attached to the substrate only in the centre, and conspicuous only when wet.

96 *Exidia plana* (formerly ***glandulosa***) – This shiny black species also has an apt English name – "Witch's Butter". Common in Europe on dead deciduous wood, it was found here below Alevkaya, Dec. 1998.

removed from stump

95 Tremella mesenterica

96 Exidia plana

growing on dead carob

Order **AURICULARIALES**   Family **AURICULARIACEAE**

Genus *AURICULARIA* (Lat. "ear-shaped"), with only two common species including this one,

97 *Auricularia auricula-judae* (Lat. "Judas' Ear", reflecting the Christian legend that the disciple Judas after betraying Jesus, hanged himself from an elder tree; on which in Europe this fungus is most commonly found). The English name "Jew's Ear" is a somewhat anti-Semitic corruption of Jesus ear.

The thin ear-like fruitbody, narrowly attached to the dead or dying tree, is dry and scurfy on the sterile outer side, reddish-brown, velvety and veined on the spore-bearing inner side, gelatinous in humid conditions but brittle when dry. EDIBLE, but not of high quality. Several fruit-bodies often fuse together, covering a large area.

The specimen shown was found on a felled *Mulberry* in Karaman, Feb. 1998.

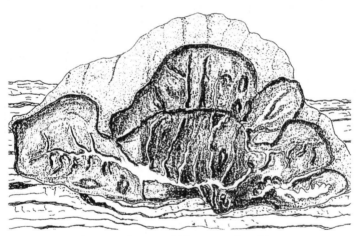

outer surface with smooth ribs,
inner (fertile) sharply wrinkled

97 Auricularia auricula-judae

Order **USTILAGINALES**   Family **USTILAGINACEAE**

With this order, finally, we come to a very different group of fungi, the "smuts", some 1000 species all parasitic on grasses or sedges and enjoying a highly complex life-cycle in which several different kinds of spores are formed at various stages. Most species belong to the *Genus USTILAGO*. There is no distinct fruitbody, but in one species,

98 Ustilago zeae, the "Maize Smut" or "Corn Cob Smut", the parasite causes gross deformities of the maize flowers and fruit. In Mexico these deformities are considered choicely EDIBLE and sold in tins. Our illustration shows an infected maize plant found in this country in July 2001.

98 *Ustilago zeae* on growing maize
- and tinned

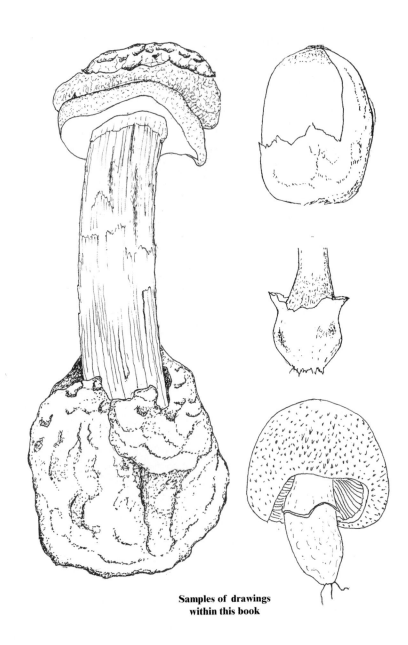

**Samples of drawings
within this book**

Index to Genus Numbers (*not* page numbers)

Polyporus 13
Psathyrella 59
Psilocybe 65
Ripartites 76
Rhizopogon 73
Rhodocybe 48r
Russula 82
Rugosomyces 42
Sarcodon 23x
Sarcosphaera 3
Scleroderma 91
Sceletocutis 19c
Schizophyllum 24
Sericeomyces 52
Stereum 22
Stropharia 64
Suillius 78
Trametes 14
Tremella 95
Tricholoma 32
Tubaria 71
Tulostoma 88
Ustilago 98
Vascellum 86
Volvariella 46
Xerocomus 79
Xeromphalina 40

Turkish and Turkish Cypriot Names
Beyaz mantar 45a
Dağ mantar 83
Gavçar mantarı 10
Kavçar mantarı 10
Kırmızı mantar 83
Laden mantari 83
Osuruk mantarı 85
Ova mantar 55
Toprak mantar 91
Yağlı mantar 46

English Names
Bird's Nest 90
Blewit 33
Bolete 77-80
Cramp Ball 7
Death Cap 45d
Earth Ball 73,91
Earth Star 84
Fly Agaric 45e
Honey Fungus 30
Ink Cap 57
Jack-O-Lantern 74
Judas Ear 97
King Arthurs Cake 07
Lawyer's Wig 57b
Magpie 57a
Miller 48m
Morel 01
Mushroom 55
Oyster Fungus 10
Puff Ball 85
Slippery Jack 78
Split Gill 23
Stinkhorn 93
Sulphur Tuft 15
Wax Cap 25, 26
Weeping Widow 59
Witches Butter 96